MATHS

FOR PRACTICE & REVISION

4

AVERAGE

SETS

OTHER BASES

ANGLES

SPEED

PETER ROBSON

Newby Books

PO BOX 40, SCARBOROUGH
NORTH YORKSHIRE, YO12 5TW
TEL/FAX 01723 362713
www.newbybooks.co.uk

A AVERAGE

The AVERAGE or MEAN of a set of numbers (or quantities) is the SUM (total) of all the numbers, divided by how many numbers there are.

$$\text{Average} = \frac{\text{Sum of quantities}}{\text{Number of quantities}}$$

e.g. (1) Find the average of 9, 3, 8, 4 and 11.

$$\text{Average} = \frac{9+3+8+4+11}{5} = \frac{35}{5} = 7$$

(2) Find the mean of £2.74, £3.27, £2.92, £3.03.

$$\text{Mean} = \frac{2.74+3.27+2.92+3.03}{4} = \frac{11.96}{4} = £2.99$$

REMEMBER   0 is counted as a number.

e.g. The average of 9, 7, 0, 5, 0, 3

$$= \frac{9+7+0+5+0+3}{6} = \frac{24}{6} = 4$$

B Finding a missing quantity

Sum of quantities = Average X Number of quantities

e.g. The average of eight numbers is 12. Seven of the numbers are 13, 7, 18, 11, 3, 10 and 20. What is the missing number?

Sum of quantities = 12 x 8 = 96

Other seven numbers add up to

$$13+7+18+11+3+10+20=82$$
so missing number is 96 − 82 = 14

e.g.(2) The average mass of three samples of metal is 49 g. If one sample has mass 58 g and another has mass 37 g, what is the mass of the third sample?

Sum of quantities = 3 x 49 g = 147 g

Other two samples have mass 58 + 37 = 95 g

so mass of third sample = 147 − 95 = 52 g.

a Find the average of each of these sets of numbers

1) 8,6,9,5
2) 36,43,38
3) 7,9,8,4,0,9,7,3,5,8
4) 117,123,121,113,131,127
5) 5.3, 6.8, 7.1, 6.4, 5.9

6) 18.55, 16.37
7) 374,389,363,328,388,350,391
8) 2.08, 1.73, 0, 3.4, 1.09
9) 9,7,4,1,1,3,8,7
10) 1276, 1253, 1315, 1292, 1308, 1254.

---

b Find the average of each of these sets of numbers

1) £6,£12,£9,£13,£15,£4,£11
2) 80,78,56,92,67,74
3) 5.3kg,3.6kg,6.1kg,4.8kg,7.7kg
4) 41,48,42,38,45,42,50,37,44
5) 82cm,85cm,89cm,94cm

6) 0,14,22,0,16,2,23,11
7) 1.9km, 3.4km, 2.3km, 3.2km
8) 5,8,9,13,12,6,10,4,7,11,14
9) £2.84, £3.18, £1.45
10) $\frac{1}{6}, \frac{2}{3}, \frac{3}{4}, \frac{7}{12}, \frac{1}{3}$

---

c Find the values of A, B, C, D and E

1) The average of 10, 5, 12, 6, A and 14 is 9
2) The mean of 128, B, 145 and 138 is 132
3) The average of 7, 0, 27, 5, C, 18 and 11 is 13
4) The average of 48, D, 61 and 52 is 53
5) The mean of 6.46, 6.55 and E is 6.66

---

d

1) The heights of five boys were 147cm, 142cm, 137cm, 123cm, and 116cm. What was their average height?
2) Sarah bought 2 cakes at 16p each and 4 cakes at 13p each. What was the average price of a cake?
3) The hours of sunshine (to the nearest half hour) for each day in a certain week were Sunday 6½ h, Monday 3 h, Tuesday 0 h, Wednesday 9½ h, Thursday 7½ h, Friday 5 h, Saturday 10½ h. What was the daily average of hours of sunshine?
4) The heights above sea level of three hilltops are 693m, 724m and 737m. Find their mean height.
5) The average thickness of nine books is 14mm. The thicknesses of eight of the books are 8mm, 9mm, 10mm, 12mm, 16mm, 16mm, 19mm and 21mm. Find the thickness of the other book.

A CLOCKS AND CALENDARS (1)

a.m. and p.m.

a.m. is short for Latin 'ante meridiem', meaning 'before noon' (before 12.00 mid-day)

p.m. is short for Latin 'post meridiem', meaning 'after noon' (after 12.00 mid-day)

e.g.	7.15 a.m.	means	7.15 in the morning
	8.40 p.m.	means	8.40 in the evening

B 24 HOUR CLOCK

To prevent confusion between a.m. and p.m., 24 hour clock is often used, especially in timetables for buses, trains, airlines, etc. The 24 hour clock begins at midnight (0000) and ends at the next midnight (2400)

To write times before 1.00 p.m. in 24 hour clock, put the same times but make sure there are always four figures

e.g.	3.15 a.m.	=	0315
	9.50 a.m.	=	0950
	11.08 a.m.	=	1108
	12.47 p.m.	=	1247

To write times from 1.00 p.m. onwards in 24 hour clock, ADD 12 TO THE HOURS

e.g.	1.00 p.m.	=	13 00	1 + **12**
	5.45 p.m.	=	17 45	5 + **12**
	10.26 p.m.	=	22 26	10 + **12**

MIDNIGHT can be written either 0000 or 2400
MIDDAY (NOON) is written 1200

Note Times from 12.01 to 12.59 **a.m.** are written 0001 to 0059
Times from 12.01 to 12.59 **p.m.** are written 1201 to 1259

C

To convert 24 hour clock times, 1300 onwards, into p.m. times, SUBTRACT 12 FROM THE HOURS

e.g.	2355	=	11.55 p.m.	23 − **12**
	1410	=	2.10 p.m.	14 − **12**
	2000	=	8.00 p.m.	20 − **12**

<u>REMEMBER</u> All times after 12.00 noon (1200) are p.m.

a Write in 24 hour clock notation

1) 6.45 a.m.	6) 4.13 p.m.	11) 3.34 a.m.
2) 11.20 a.m.	7) 12.00 noon	12) 9.05 p.m.
3) 1.35 p.m.	8) 9.53 a.m.	13) 10.17 a.m.
4) 2.00 a.m.	9) 2.10 p.m.	14) 6.58 p.m.
5) 8.32 p.m.	10) 10.45 p.m.	15) 11.11 p.m.

b Write in 24 hour clock notation

1) 8.00 a.m.	6) 9.30 p.m.	11) 5.55 p.m.
2) 3.15 p.m.	7) 5.49 a.m.	12) 10.37 p.m.
3) 7.27 p.m.	8) 4.02 p.m.	13) 1.12 a.m.
4) 12.40 p.m.	9) 12.25 a.m.	14) 6.46 p.m.
5) 4.51 a.m.	10) 3.50 a.m.	15) 11.22 p.m.

c Write in a.m. or p.m. notation

1) 0430	6) 2020	11) 1432
2) 1911	7) 1316	12) 1025
3) 1540	8) 0044	13) 1709
4) 0756	9) 1227	14) 0848
5) 1105	10) 2250	15) 2351

d

1) Copy this (imaginary) bus timetable, writing all the times in 24 hour clock.

		a.m.	p.m.	p.m.	p.m.
Orbrook	depart	9.45	2.15	3.45	7.30
Beck Edge	depart	9.55	2.25	3.55	7.40
Norford	depart	10.01	2.31	4.01	7.46
Russet Colbury	depart	10.09	2.39	4.09	7.54
Brackenhurst	depart	10.16	2.46	4.16	8.01
Tiddingfield	depart	10.23	2.53	4.23	8.08
Great Gorton	depart	10.34	3.04	4.34	8.19
Walby	arrive	10.40	3.10	4.40	8.25

2) Another bus sets off (departs) from Orbrook at 10.20 p.m. and takes exactly the same times as the other buses. Write out the full timetable for this bus, starting Orbrook depart 2220.

CLOCKS AND CALENDARS (2)

A Hours and minutes

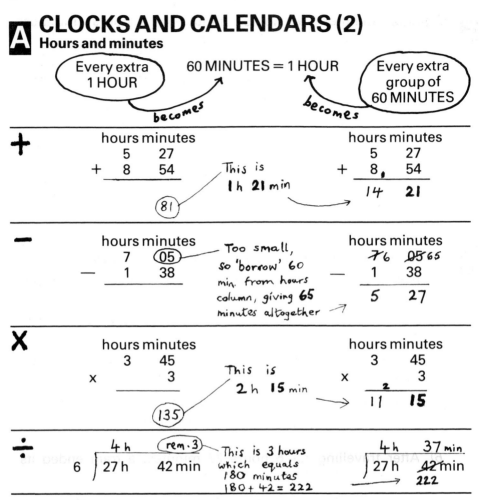

Every extra 1 HOUR becomes

60 MINUTES = 1 HOUR

Every extra group of 60 MINUTES becomes

+

hours	minutes
5	27
+ 8	54
	(81)

This is
1 h 21 min

hours	minutes
5	27
+ 8,	54
14	21

−

hours	minutes
7	(05)
− 1	38

Too small, so 'borrow' 60 min. from hours column, giving **65** minutes altogether

hours	minutes
7̶6	0̶5̶ 65
− 1	38
5	27

X

hours	minutes
3	45
x	3
	(135)

This is
2 h 15 min

hours	minutes
3	45
x	3
11	15

÷

4 h — (rem. 3)

6) 27 h   42 min

This is 3 hours which equals 180 minutes
180 + 42 = 222

4 h   37 min

) 27 h   4̶2̶ min
          222

B Problems

e.g. (1) A ship set off at 0950 and travelled for 7 hours 45 minutes. At what time did it complete its journey?

hours	minutes
09	50
+ 7,	45
17	35 (95)

It completed its journey at 1735

e.g. (2) A helicopter made 5 journeys which took a total time of 8h 30 min. If all the journeys took the same amount of time, how long did each journey take?

1 h   42 min

5) 8 h   3̶0̶ min
           210

Each journey took 1 h 42 min

a

1) hours	minutes
7	43
+ 2	51

2) hours	minutes
14	27
+ 6	49

3) hours	minutes
1	25
x	4

4) hours	minutes
4	55
+ 3	26

5) hours	minutes
8	06
− 1	24

6) hours	minutes
2	39
1	54
+ 3	47

7) hours	minutes
3	38
x	5

8) hours	minutes
13	12
− 7	47

9) 5 ⟌ 16 h   15 min

10) 3 ⟌ 8 h   15 min

b

1) A bus sets off on a journey at 1135 and travels for 2 hours 41 minutes At what time does it complete its journey?

2) If each lesson lasts 35 minutes, how long, in hours and minutes, do 8 lessons last?

3) Some cricketers started a match at 1030 and finished it at 1512. How long did the match last?

4) On a car journey of 10 hours 20 minutes, 4 people shared the driving equally. For how long did each person drive?

5) The four pieces of music in a concert lasted 8 minutes, 26 minutes, 15 minutes and 46 minutes. How long, in hours and minutes, did the music last altogether?

6) After travelling for 6 hours 27 minutes, a train ended its journey at 2203. At what time did it begin its journey?

7) An airliner takes 2 h 37 min to do a certain journey. Find how long 5 journeys of this length would take.

8) A satellite took 22 h 38 min to go round the Earth 7 times. How long did it take to go round once?

9) John had 4 hours of free time. He divided the time equally between playing football, writing a story and planning a new hutch for his rabbit. How much time, in hours and minutes, did he spend on each activity?

10) Each day a village shop opens at 0815 and closes at 1300 for lunch. Then it opens again at 1400 and closes at 1900. (a) For how long is it open each day? (b) If it opens every day of the week, including Sunday, for how long is it open each week?

CLOCKS AND CALENDARS (3)

A Going past midnight

When adding a time from one day to the next, SUBTRACT 24 HOURS from your answer.

e.g. A ship left Liverpool at 2215 and took 8 h 50 min to reach Dublin. At what time did the ship arrive in Dublin?

h	min		h	min	
22	15		31	05	The ship arrived
+ 8	50		− 24	00	in Dublin at 0705
31	05		07	05	the next day

When subtracting a time from one day to the previous day (the day before) 'BORROW' 24 HOURS before you start.

e.g. A train set off from Newcastle at 1950 on Friday and reached Plymouth at 0456 on Saturday. How long did its journey take?

h	min		h	min	
04	56	+ 24 HOURS =	28	56	
−19	50		−19	50	
			9	06	The train took
					9 hours 6 minutes

B Average times

$$\text{Average} = \frac{\text{Sum of quantities}}{\text{Number of quantities}}$$

e.g. A train's arrival times on the days of a certain week were 2006, 1955, 2002, 1954, 1953, 1958, 2005. What was its average time of arrival?

h	min
20	06
19	55
20	02
19	54
19	53
19	58
+ 20	05
139	53 (233)

```
        h     min
        19    59
   7 ) 139    53
       rem.6  413
```

Average time of arrival of train was 19 59

a

1) Martin went to sleep at 2237 and slept for 8 hours 47 minutes. At what time did he wake up?

2) On a certain evening the sun set at 1944 and rose the next morning at 0407. Calculate the length of time between sunset and sunrise.

3) A train left Stirling at 2223 and arrived in London 7 hours 39 minutes later. At what time did it arrive in London?

4) A night porter at a hotel began work at 2315 and finished work at 0500 the next morning. How long did he work?

5) An airliner left London at 2045 and travelled to Accra, arriving there at 0336 the next day. How long did its journey take?

6) Aunt Lucy set off from Liverpool at 1950 and drove to Southampton. The journey took 7 h 27 min. At what time did she reach Southampton?

7) A shop opens from 0715 until 2030 each day. How long is it from closing time each evening until opening time the next morning?

8) A group of long-distance walkers started a walk on Saturday evening. Their walk took them 11 hours 35 minutes and they finished it at 0920 on Sunday morning. At what time did they start?

9) David set off on a journey at 1425 on Wednesday and reached the end of his journey at 1150 on Friday. How long, in hours and minutes, did the journey take?

10) A swimming pool began to be filled with water at 1840 on Monday evening. The pool took 26 h 35 min to fill. At what time on which day was the pool full?

---

b

1) Find the average of 6 h 37 min, 5 h 42 min and 6 h 29 min.

2) Find the average of 3 h 14 min, 2 h 48 min, 1 h 57 min, 2 h 22 min, 1 h 54 min.

3) On six days of a certain week a train arrived in Bristol at 1540, 1549, 1545, 1543, 1548 and 1539. (a) What was its average time of arrival? (b) If it should have arrived at 1545 each day, how many minutes early or late was it on average?

4) What is the average of 5 h 8 min, 4 h 39 min, 5 h 26 min, 4 h 15 min?

5) School began at 0855. One week Peter arrived at school at 0841, 0852, 0846, 0838 and 0843. Find out the daily average number of minutes he was early for school.

A CLOCKS AND CALENDARS (4)
Years and months

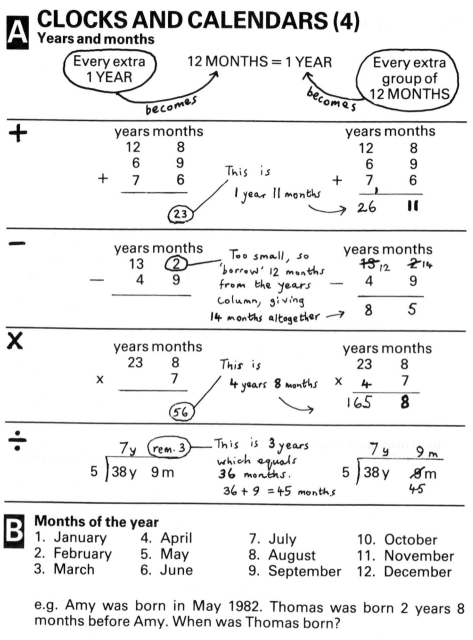

Every extra 1 YEAR

12 MONTHS = 1 YEAR

Every extra group of 12 MONTHS

becomes

becomes

+

years	months
12	8
6	9
+ 7	6
	(23)

This is 1 year 11 months

years	months
12	8
6	9
+ 7	6
26	11

−

years	months
13	(2)
− 4	9

Too small, so 'borrow' 12 months from the years column, giving 14 months altogether →

years	months
13 12	2 14
− 4	9
8	5

X

years	months
23	8
×	7
	(56)

This is 4 years 8 months

years	months
23	8
× 4	7
165	8

÷

7y (rem. 3)

5) 38 y 9 m

This is 3 years which equals 36 months. 36 + 9 = 45 months

7y   9 m

5) 38 y   ~~9~~ m
          45

B Months of the year

1. January
2. February
3. March
4. April
5. May
6. June
7. July
8. August
9. September
10. October
11. November
12. December

e.g. Amy was born in May 1982. Thomas was born 2 years 8 months before Amy. When was Thomas born?

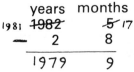

	years	months
1981	~~1982~~	~~5~~ 17
−	2	8
	1979	9

Thomas was born in September 1979

a

1) years months
```
      5     6
      4     2
  +   3    11
  _____
```

2) years months
```
      7     9
  x         3
  _____
```

3) years months
```
     24     2
  −  18     9
  _____
```

4) years months
```
     13     8
  x         5
  _____
```

5) 3 ⟌17 y 6 m

6) years months
```
     36    10
     37    10
  +  33     3
  _____
```

7) 7 ⟌25 y 1 m

8) years months
```
      5     0
  −   1    10
  _____
```

9) years months
```
     19     3
  x         4
  _____
```

10) years months
```
     45     1
  −  27     5
  _____
```

b

1) Sally's three dogs are aged 5 years 7 months, 3 years 4 months and 1 year 9 months. What is the sum of their ages?

2) Simon was born in August 1977. His brother Lee was born 3 years 9 months later. In which month of which year was Lee born?

3) The battle of Waterloo took place in June 1815. The battle of Trafalgar was fought 9 years 8 months earlier. When was the battle of Trafalgar?

4) Bill is 8 years 11 months old. His father is 4 times Bill's age. How old is his father?

5) Three girls were aged 13 years 4 months, 11 years 0 months and 9 years 11 months. By first finding the sum of their ages, calculate their average age.

6) Mr. Green's car was new in January 1987; Mr. Brown's car was new in May 1979. In years and months, how much older than Mr. Green's car is Mr. Brown's car?

7) Ian was born in March 1986. His cousin Andrew was born 7 years 4 months before Ian. When was Andrew born?

8) Lisa's age is 5 times the age of her youngest brother. Lisa is 14 years 7 months old. How old is her youngest brother?

9) King Edward I of England reigned from November 1272 until July 1307. How long, in years and months, did he reign?

10) Jim is 9 years 9 months old, Tom is 11 years 3 months old, George is 9 years 10 months old and Peter is 10 years 6 months old. Find (a) the sum of their ages, (b) their average age.

A SETS (1)

A set is a group or collection of things.
Each thing in a set is called a MEMBER or ELEMENT.

The set of can be written { }

e.g. 'the set of days of the week' can be written
{days of the week}
'the set of wild animals' can be written
{wild animals}

A set can also be written out in full to show all its MEMBERS,
e.g. 'the set of seasons' can be written {winter, autumn, spring,
summer}

Members of a set may be written in any order.

B

$\in$ means 'is a member of'
e.g. autumn is a member of the set of seasons can be written

autumn $\in$ {seasons}

blue is a member of the set of colours can be written
blue $\in$ {colours}

$\notin$ means 'is NOT a member of'

e.g. sheepdog is not a member of the set of prime numbers

sheepdog $\notin$ {prime numbers}

C

Sets are often given a capital letter name to identify them, e.g.

A	=	{animals}
P	=	{prime numbers}
T	=	{pupils in Form 3} , etc.

D

How to draw the brackets for sets

For the beginning of the set, draw a very thin S with a very thin
backwards S underneath. For the end of the set, draw them the
other way round.

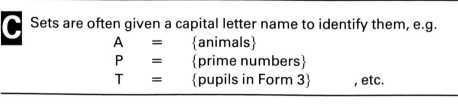

a Write, using brackets

e.g. The set of trees   =   {trees}

1) The set of seasons
2) The set of triangles
3) The set of spaceships
4) The set of tortoises
5) The set of books
6) The set of puddings
7) The set of ghosts
8) The set of sailing boats
9) The set of birds
10) The set of pyramids

b Write, using letters and brackets
e.g. Set A is the set of alligators   A   =   {alligators}

1) Set C is the set of African countries
2) Set Z is the set of footballs
3) Set H is the set of hamsters
4) Set S is the set of sausages
5) Set F is the set of flowers

c Write, using signs $\in$, $\notin$ and brackets
e.g. Venus is a member of the set of planets

Venus $\in$ {planets}

1) N is a member of the set of letters
2) Charles is a member of the set of boys' names
3) sugar is not a member of the set of animals
4) 23 is a member of the set of prime numbers
5) Finland is not a member of the set of colours
6) tennis is not a member of the set of English kings
7) oxygen is a member of the set of elements
8) oak is a member of the set of trees
9) * is not a member of the set of ponies
10) apple pie is a member of the set of pies

SETS (2)

A

Venn diagrams

A Venn diagram is a way of showing sets in picture form. Each set is drawn as a rough circle, ring or egg shape.

e.g. Set A as a Venn diagram would be drawn

e.g. Set F = {cod, haddock, plaice}   would be drawn

The space inside a Venn diagram is called a REGION.
Venn diagrams were named after their inventor, the Reverend John Venn (born 1834, died 1923).

B

Empty set

An empty set is a set which contains no members. It is also called a NULL set or a VOID set. It can be written either $\emptyset$ or { }

e.g. If set S is the set of four-cornered triangles
$$S = \emptyset \quad \text{or} \quad S = \{\,\}$$

If G is the set of giraffes fitted with
diesel engines
$$G = \emptyset \quad \text{or} \quad G = \{\,\}$$

C

Number of members of a set is written n   followed by the name of the set in ordinary brackets

e.g. If set V = {A, E, I, O, U} the number of members in the set is 5, so
$$n(V) = 5$$

If set W = {Monday, Tuesday, Wednesday, Thursday, Friday, Saturday, Sunday}
$$n(W) = 7$$

If set D = {3}
$$n(D) = 1$$

The number of members of an empty set is 0

e.g. If set J = $\emptyset$, n (J) = 0

a Draw a Venn diagram to show each of these sets
1) Set B = {John, Michael, Roger}
2) Set P = {2, 3, 5, 7, 11, 13, 17, 19}
3) Set L = {London, Lisbon, Leeds, Los Angeles, Liverpool}
4) Set J = ∅
5) Set D = {N, E, S, W}
6) Set S = {21, 36, 55, 60, 67, 68, 92, 93, 125}
7) Set V = {carrot, onion}
8) Set Y = {}
9) Set O = {Pacific, Atlantic, Indian, Arctic}
10) Set E = {+, —, ×, ÷}

b For each of the sets in part **a** (the questions at the top of the page), copy and complete the following to show the number of members of each set
1) n(B) =
2) n(P) =
3) n(L) =
4) n(J) =
5) n(D) =
6) n(S) =
7) n(V) =
8) n(Y) =
9) n(O) =
10) n(E) =

c List the members of each of these sets, e.g.
W. The set of days of the week.
W = {Sunday, Monday, Tuesday, Wednesday, Thursday, Friday, Saturday}
If there are no members, write ∅
1) A. The set of odd numbers between 0 and 10
2) B. The set of seasons of the year
3) C. The set of five-sided triangles
4) D. The set of names of months beginning with the letter J
5) E. The set of integers greater than −6 but less than −1
6) F. The set of prime numbers between 20 and 30
7) G. The set of jellies that can ride bicycles
8) H. The set of letters of the alphabet after g but before n
9) I. The set of invisible things which can be seen
10) J. The set of multiples of 6 which are less than 25

A SETS (3)
SUBSETS

A SUBSET is a set which is a small part of another set

e.g. {maths teachers} is a subset of {teachers}

    {alarm clocks} is a subset of {clocks}

    {6, 7, 8} is a subset of {5, 6, 7, 8, 9, 10}

The sign $\subset$ means 'is a SUBSET of'

e.g. {green cars} $\subset$ {cars}

    {B, C} $\subset$ {A, B, C}

B Listing all the subsets of a set

e.g. (1) The subsets of {apple, banana} are

    {apple, banana},   {apple},   {banana},   ∅

e.g. (2) The subsets of {1, 3, 5} are

    {1, 3, 5},   {1, 3},   {1, 5},   {3, 5},   {1},   {3},   {5},   ∅

REMEMBER (1) A set is a subset of itself

e.g. {horses} $\subset$ {horses}

(2) An empty set is a subset of any other set

e.g.   ∅ $\subset$ {A, E, I, O, U}

(3) Members of a set may be written in any order

e.g. {1, 5} is the same set as {5, 1}

C

Venn diagram of a subset is drawn as a smaller ring inside a larger ring

e.g.   D = {ducks}

       N = {noisy ducks}

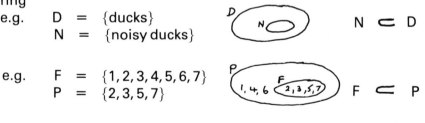

N $\subset$ D

e.g.   F = {1, 2, 3, 4, 5, 6, 7}

       P = {2, 3, 5, 7}

F $\subset$ P

NOTE. In a Venn diagram, each member may be written ONLY ONCE

D Contains as a subset

⊃ means 'contains as a subset'

e.g.   If {British mountains} $\subset$ {mountains}

then   {mountains} ⊃ {British mountains}

    ⊄ means 'is NOT a subset of'

    ⊅ means 'does NOT contain as a subset'

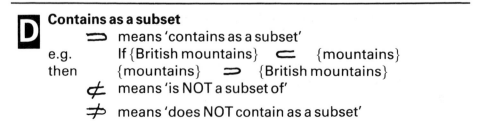

a Write in short, using ⊂
e.g. A is a subset of B   A ⊂ B

1) {brick walls} is a subset of {walls}
2) {Scotsmen} is a subset of {men}
3) Q is a subset of P
4) {fizzy drinks} is a subset of {drinks}
5) {B, C, D} is a subset of {A, B, C, D, E}

---

b Write in short, using ⊂, ⊄, ∈, ∉, ∅, { }
1) {frying pan} is not a subset of {animals}
2) violin is a member of the set of instruments
3) G is an empty set
4) lollipop is not a member of the set of gorillas
5) {3, 5, 7} is a subset of {1, 3, 5, 7, 9, 11}

---

c Make a list of all the subsets of each set
1) {cabbage, turnip}
2) {Emma, Kate, Tina}
3) {1, 2, 3, 4}
4) {red, blue, green}
5) {P, Q, R, S, T}

---

d Draw a Venn diagram to show each of the following.
Put each member in its correct region

1) {24, 36} is a subset of {12, 24, 36, 48, 60}
2) {pine, larch} is a subset of {oak, pine, beech, larch}
3) {f, g, h} is a subset of {a, b, c, d, e, f, g, h}
4) {deuce} is a subset of {love, 15, 30, 40, advantage, deuce}
5) {9, 10, 11, 12} is a subset of {9, 10, 11, 12, 13}

---

e For each of these pairs of sets, draw a Venn diagram showing the
subset inside the larger set. Remember that each member may be
written only once

1) {cricket, tennis}; {cricket, hockey, netball, tennis}
2) {P, Q, R, S, T}; {P, R, T}
3) {wasp, bee, hornet};
     {butterfly, bee, wasp, dragonfly, hornet, ladybird}
4) {yellow, green, red, blue}; {red}
5) {5, 6, 7, 8, 9}; {7, 8}

A SETS (4)

Intersection ('CAP')

Two (or more) different sets may have one or more members in common. The shared set which contains these members is called the INTERSECTION of the original sets.

Intersection is written ∩ and often called CAP

e.g. Set L = {a, b, c, d, e, f}
      Set V = {a, e, i, o, u}

The members a and e are members of **both sets** so {a, e} is the intersection of sets L and V (L cap V).

$$\text{Set } L \cap V = \{a, e\}$$

B

In a Venn diagram, intersection is shown by overlapping

e.g. L = {a, b, c, d, e, f}
      V = {a, e, i, o, u}
      L ∩ V = {a, e}

The region in the middle
is the set L ∩ V,
the intersection of sets L and V

---

e.g (2)
J = {James, John, Joseph, Jennifer}
G = {Christine, Jennifer, Sara}
J ∩ G = {Jennifer}

---

e.g. (3)
A = {h, j, k, o, v}
B = {h, k, o, p, t}
C = {g, k, p, q, t, v}
A ∩ B = {h, o, k}
A ∩ C = {v, k}
B ∩ C = {p, t, k}

The very middle region is called A ∩ B ∩ C

A ∩ B ∩ C = {k}

a Find the intersection of each of these pairs of sets
e.g. A = {1, 2, 3}, B = {2, 3, 5, 7}. **Answer** A∩B = {2, 3}

1) C = {k, m, n, p, q, r}, D = {j, k, p, r, s, t}
2) E = {5, 10, 15, 20, 25}, F = {10, 20, 30, 40, 50}
3) G = {Matthew, Mark, Luke, John}, H = {Carl, Peter, James}
4) J = {$\frac{5}{4}$, $\frac{8}{3}$, $\frac{16}{15}$, $\frac{9}{4}$, $\frac{11}{6}$, $\frac{11}{4}$, $\frac{7}{4}$}, K = {$\frac{1}{4}$, $\frac{3}{4}$, $\frac{5}{4}$, $\frac{7}{4}$, $\frac{9}{4}$, $\frac{11}{4}$}
5) L = { ⚅ ⚄ ⚃ ⚄ }, M = { ⚀ ⚁ ⚂ }

---

b Draw a larger copy of the Venn diagram to show each pair of sets. Write each member in its correct region

1) Z = {%, ⌢, <, ÷}, Y = { ✓, %, +}
2) A = {4, 8, 12, 16, 20}, S = {1, 4, 9, 16, 25}
3) H = {Britten, Bach, Bizet}, J = {Beethoven, Bruch, Bach}
4) U = {f, g, h, i, j, k,}, V = {g, h, i, j, k, l, m}
5) C = {4, 5, 6, 7, 8}, E = {2, 4, 6, 8}

---

c Draw a larger copy of the Venn diagram to show each group of sets. Write each member in its correct region

1) A = {2, 4, 6, 8, 10}, B = {1, 2, 3, 4}, C = {4, 8, 12, 16}
2) P = {a, b, c, e, h, j, k}, Q = {e, f, g, h, j, k, m}
R = {c, d, e, f, g,}
3) W = {■, ▽, ★, ◇}, X = {★, O, ◇, ◆},
Y = {☆, ◇, ●, ◆, ★}
4) J = {2, 3, 5, 7}, K = {2, 3, 4, 6}, L = {3, 5, 6, 8}
5) F = {Dan, Jim, Joe, Sam}, M = {Ben, Dan, Pat, Tom},
T = {Ben, Bob, Dan, Joe, Tom}

---

d For each of these groups of sets, draw the best possible Venn diagram and write each member in its correct region
1) C = {x, y, z}, D = {v, w, x, y, z}
2) R = {19, 23, 29, 31, 37}, T = {31, 37, 41, 43}
3) K = { ʎ, Ƴ, ⱶ, ⊣ }, M = { Ⴕ, Ƴ, ʜ }
4) F = {2½, 5½, 6½, 7½, 9½}, P = {5½}
5) B = {p, s, t, w, y}, E = {q, s, t, v, w, y},
G = {s, t, w, y, z}

A SETS (5)
Union ('CUP')

The UNION of two (or more) sets is the **set containing all the members** of both (or all) sets.

Union is written U and often called CUP

e.g. P = {Thames, Tay, Tees, Trent, Tweed}
Q = {Clyde, Tay, Tweed, Dee, Forth}

The union of sets P and Q is

P U Q = {Thames, Trent, Tees, Tay, Tweed, Clyde, Dee, Forth}

NOTE Each member of the union should be listed ONLY ONCE. Do NOT repeat any members (e.g. do **not** write Tay, Tay, Tweed, Tweed)

Union of three sets is written A U B U C , etc.

B Venn diagrams to show H.C.F. and L.C.M.

e.g. Find the H.C.F. and L.C.M. of 24 and 90 by drawing a Venn diagram

1) Express 24 and 90 as products of prime factors

2	24
2	12
2	6
3	3
	1

2	90
3	45
3	15
5	5
	1

2) Draw a Venn diagram and write down the factors

24 2, 2,   2, 3, 90
    2, 3   3, 5

3) If any factors are **common** to both (or all) sets, write them in the intersection and rub out (or cross out) the originals

24 2, 2 (2,3) 3, 5 90

H.C.F. = 24 ∩ 90 = 2 x 3 = **6**

L.C.M. = 24 U 90 = 2 x 2 x 2 x 3 x 3 x 5

or $2^3 \times 3^2 \times 5$ = **360**

a Find the union of these pairs of sets
e.g. Y = {27, 28, 29, 30}, Z = {20, 30, 40}

Answer Y **U** Z = {20, 27, 28, 29, 30, 40}

1) A = {4, 5, 6, 7}, K = {1, 2, 3, 4, 5, 6}
2) T = {red, yellow, green}, B = {blue, green, black, red}
3) Q = {a, b, c, d, e}, R = {a, b, c}
4) J = {January, June, July}, M = {July, August, September}
5) P = {2, 3, 5, 7, 11, 13}, N = {4, 8, 12, 16}

---

b Find the intersection (**∩**) and union (**U**) of each of these pairs of sets

1) B = {rook, blackbird, starling}, C = {bishop, knight, rook}
2) T = {Ω, Τ, Γ, Σ}, V = {Γ, Ρ, Υ, Τ, Ω}
3) F = {iron, zinc, copper, chromium, cadmium}
   G = {carbon, cadmium, chlorine, chromium, copper}
4) N = {e, f, g, h, j}, Q = {c, d}
5) D = {9, 11}, K = {8, 9, 10, 11, 12}

---

c Find the H.C.F. and L.C.M. of each group of numbers. Draw a Venn diagram of each answer

1) 120, 45
2) 84, 154
3) 96, 48
4) 35, 56
5) 24, 64
6) 110, 66
7) 180, 168
8) 270, 234
9) 18, 48, 84
10) 24, 44, 60

---

d Look at the Venn diagram. Copy the questions and complete them with the correct answers

e.g. R = { } **Answer** R = {3, 6, 9, 12, 15}

1) T = { }
2) R∩T = { }
3) n (R) =
4) P**U**R = { }
5) n (P) =
6) P∩T =
7) P**U**V = { }
8) V ⊂
9) n (R∩T) =
10) V∩P = { }

SETS (6)

A **Disjoint sets** are sets which have nothing in common. They do not share any members.

e.g. (1) A = {1, 2, 3, 4},   B = {8, 9} are DISJOINT sets

(2) S = {a, b, c},   T = {☐, △, ☆} are DISJOINT sets

In a Venn diagram, disjoint sets are shown as unconnected regions, e.g.

F= {21, 22, 23},   G = {w, x, y, z}

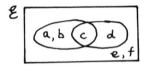

The intersection of disjoint sets is always an empty set

B **Universal set** is the set containing **everything** you are dealing with. It is usually shown by the sign $\mathcal{E}$. All other sets are subsets of the universal set.

The Venn diagram of the universal set is usually drawn as a rectangle

e.g.

$\mathcal{E}$ [a, b (c) d   e, f] $\mathcal{E}$ = {a, b, c, d, e, f}

C **'NOT' (Complement of a set)**

The complement of a set contains all the members of the universal set which are not in the set.

The complement of set A is written A′

e.g.

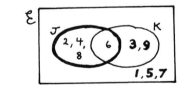

The complement of J (sometimes called **NOT J**)

J′ = {1, 3, 5, 7, 9}

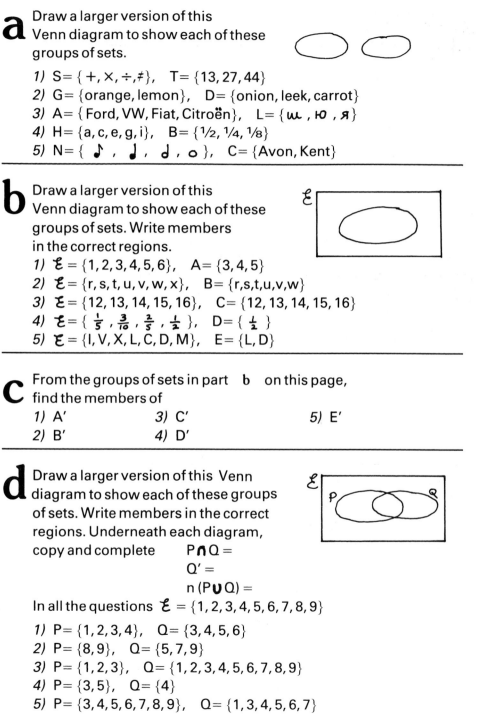

a Draw a larger version of this Venn diagram to show each of these groups of sets.

1) S= { +, ×, ÷, ≠},   T= {13, 27, 44}
2) G= {orange, lemon},   D= {onion, leek, carrot}
3) A= { Ford, VW, Fiat, Citroën},   L= { ա , ю , я }
4) H= {a, c, e, g, i},   B= {½, ¼, ⅛}
5) N= { ♪ , ♩ , ♫ , o },   C= {Avon, Kent}

b Draw a larger version of this Venn diagram to show each of these groups of sets. Write members in the correct regions.

1) ℰ = {1, 2, 3, 4, 5, 6},   A= {3, 4, 5}
2) ℰ = {r, s, t, u, v, w, x},   B= {r,s,t,u,v,w}
3) ℰ = {12, 13, 14, 15, 16},   C= {12, 13, 14, 15, 16}
4) ℰ= { $\frac{1}{5}$, $\frac{3}{10}$, $\frac{2}{5}$, $\frac{1}{2}$ },   D= { $\frac{1}{2}$ }
5) ℰ = {I, V, X, L, C, D, M},   E= {L, D}

c From the groups of sets in part b on this page, find the members of

1) A′   3) C′   5) E′
2) B′   4) D′

d Draw a larger version of this Venn diagram to show each of these groups of sets. Write members in the correct regions. Underneath each diagram, copy and complete   P∩Q =
                    Q′ =
                    n (P∪Q) =

In all the questions ℰ = {1, 2, 3, 4, 5, 6, 7, 8, 9}

1) P= {1, 2, 3, 4},   Q= {3, 4, 5, 6}
2) P= {8, 9},   Q= {5, 7, 9}
3) P= {1, 2, 3},   Q= {1, 2, 3, 4, 5, 6, 7, 8, 9}
4) P= {3, 5},   Q= {4}
5) P= {3, 4, 5, 6, 7, 8, 9},   Q= {1, 3, 4, 5, 6, 7}

A SETS (7) Revision

SET SIGNS

Make sure you know what all these signs mean

∈ is a member of   ℰ universal set
∉ is not a member of   n number of members of
⊂ is a subset of   {   } the set of
∩ intersection (CAP)   ∅ empty set
∪ union (CUP)   A′ not A (complement of A)

B

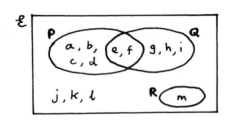

The universal set contains the sets P, Q and R

ℰ = {a, b, c, d, e, f, g, h, i, j, k, l, m}

P = {a, b, c, d, e, f}	(P∪Q)′ = {j, k, l, m}
Q = {e, f, g, h, i}	(P∩Q)′ = {a, b, c, d, g,
R = {m}	h, i, j, k, l, m}
P∩Q = {e, f}	(P∪Q∪R)′ = {j, k, l}
P∩R = ∅	P∩Q′ = {a, b, c, d}
Q∩R = ∅	P′∩Q = {g, h, i}
P∩Q∩R = ∅	n (P) = 6
P∪Q = {a, b, c, d, e, f, g, h, i}	n (Q) = 5
P∪R = {a, b, c, d, e, f, m}	n (R) = 1
Q∪R = {e, f, g, h, i, m}	n (ℰ) = 13
P∪Q∪R = {a, b, c, d, e, f, g,	n (P∩Q) = 2
h, i, m}	n (P∪R) = 7
P′ = {g, h, i, j, k, l, m}	R ⊂ ℰ
Q′ = {a, b, c, d, j, k, l, m}	c ∈ P
R′ = {a, b, c, d, e, f, g, h,	k ∉ Q etc.
i, j, k, l}	

a

Copy and complete the questions

1) H= { ....
2) J= { ....
3) H ∩ J = { .....
4) H' = { ....
5) n (J') = ...

6) n (H ∪ J)= ....
7) H ∩ J' = { ....
8) H' ∩ J' = { ....
9) H' ∪ J'= { ....
10) n (Ɛ) = { ....

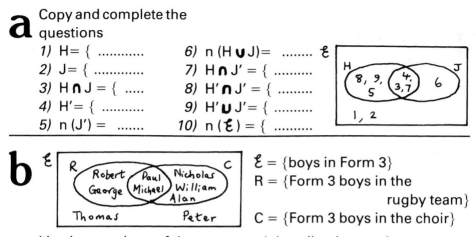

Ɛ

H ... J
8, 9, 5 4, 3,7 6
1, 2

b

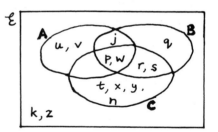

Ɛ

R ... C
Robert Paul Nicholas
George Michael William
Alan
Thomas   Peter

Ɛ = {boys in Form 3}
R = {Form 3 boys in the rugby team}
C = {Form 3 boys in the choir}

List the members of these sets and describe the sets in writing

e.g.   R ∩ C' = {George, Robert} = {Form 3 boys who are in the rugby team but not in the choir}

1) R ∩ C =
2) R' =
3) R ∪ C =

4) (R ∪ C)'=
5) R' ∩ C =

c

Ɛ = {j, k, n, p, q, r, s, t, u, v, w, x, y, z}

A = {j, p, u, v, w}
B = {j, p, q, r, s, w}
C = {n, p, r, s, t, w, x, y}

Copy and complete these questions

Ɛ

A ... B
u, v   j   q
p, w
r, s
t, x, y,
n
C
k, z

1) A ∩ B = { ....
2) C' = { ....
3) n (B) = ...
4) A ∪ B ∪ C = { ....
5) A ∩ B ∩ C= { ....
6) {x, y} ⊂ ....
7) n (A ∩ C) = ...
8) r ⊄ ....

9) C ∩ A' = { ....
10) n (Ɛ) = ...
11) A ∩ B' = { ....
12) n (B') = ...
13) u ∈ ....
14) (A ∪ B ∪ C)' = { ....
15) A ∩ C ∩ B' = { ....

A SETS (8)
Using a Venn Diagram

e.g.   Draw a Venn diagram to show the correct
NUMBER OF MEMBERS in each region

18 boxes altogether (set ε)
5 empty boxes (set B)

Empty boxes   is a subset of   boxes.
There are $(18-5) = 13$ boxes which are NOT empty (set B')
so the Venn diagram is drawn

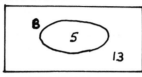

B

e.g. Draw a Venn diagram to show the correct
NUMBER OF MEMBERS in each region

47 passengers altogether (set ε)
8 French passengers (set F)
6 Austrian passengers (set A)

Sets F and A are **disjoint** subsets of set ε .   Apart from
French and Austrian passengers there are $(47-8-6)$
$= 33$ passengers, so the Venn diagram is drawn

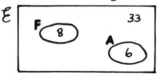

C

e.g. Draw a Venn diagram to show the correct
NUMBER OF MEMBERS in each region

60 books altogether (set ε)
34 new books (set N)
19 history books (set H)
7 new history books (set N ∩ H)

There are 7 new history books, so there are $(34-7) = 27$ new books
which are not history books, and $(19-7) = 12$ history books
which are not new. This leaves $(60-7-27-12) = 14$ books
which are neither new books nor history books, so the Venn
diagram is drawn

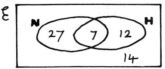

a For each pair of sets, draw a Venn diagram with the same pattern as the one on page 26 **A** Place the correct NUMBER OF MEMBERS in each region.

1) 21 sheep altogether (set ξ), 6 black sheep (set B)
2) 13 trees altogether (set ξ) 4 pine trees (set P)
3) 55 coins altogether (set ξ), 18 gold coins (set G)
4) 12 footballs altogether (set ξ), 5 leather footballs (set L)
5) 313 people altogether (set ξ), 29 Welsh people (set W)

---

b For each group of sets, draw a Venn diagram with the same pattern as the one on page 26 **B**. Place the correct NUMBER OF MEMBERS in each region.

1) 25 balloons altogether (set ξ), 7 green balloons (set G),
   8 red balloons (set R)
2) 16 boats altogether (set ξ), 8 rowing boats (set R),
   5 sailing boats (set S)
3) 43 fruits altogether (set ξ), 9 peaches (set P), 16 apples (set A)
4) 100 books altogether (set ξ), 19 history books (set H),
   28 science books (set S)
5) 22 people altogether (set ξ), 12 boys (set B), 10 girls (set G)

---

c For each group of sets, draw a Venn diagram with the same pattern as the one on page 26 **C**. Place the correct NUMBER OF MEMBERS in each region.

1) 42 cars altogether (set ξ), 11 blue cars (set B), 10 French cars
   (set F), 4 blue French cars (set B$\cap$F)
2) 18 girls altogether (set ξ), 6 girls in the orchestra (set O),
   5 girls in the netball team (set N), 3 girls in both the orchestra
   and the netball team (set O$\cap$N)
3) 21 cities altogether (set ξ), 6 capital cities (set C),
   7 German cities (set G), 2 German capital cities (set G$\cap$C)
4) 15 boys altogether (set ξ), 4 boys play ONLY soccer (set S$\cap$R'),
   3 boys play ONLY rugger (set R$\cap$S'), 2 boys play neither
   soccer nor rugger (set (S$\cup$R)')
5) 17 castles altogether (set ξ), 12 ruined castles (set R),
   10 Scottish castles (set S), 8 ruined Scottish castles (set R$\cap$S).

SETS (9)
A Using a Venn Diagram (2)

e.g. This Venn diagram shows the NUMBER of members of each set.

$\mathcal{E}$ = {pupils}

F = {pupils who play football}

H = {pupils who play hockey}

24 pupils altogether   n($\mathcal{E}$) = 24

17 play football   n (F) = 17

14 play hockey   n (H) = 14

10 play both football and hockey   n (F ∩ H) = 10

*Fill in the INTERSECTION first. Then, if 10 pupils play both football and hockey, (17-10) = 7 play ONLY football, and (14-10) = 4 play ONLY hockey. This makes a total of (7+10+4) = 21 so (24-21)= 3 play NEITHER football nor hockey.

B

e.g. (2) $\mathcal{E}$= {cows},   C = {contented cows}

F = {fat cows},   J = {Jersey cows}

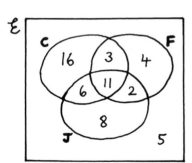

55 cows altogether

36 contented cows

20 fat cows

27 Jersey cows

11 are fat contented Jersey cows

3 are not Jersey cows, but they are fat and contented

6 are contented Jersey cows which are not fat

2 are fat Jersey cows which are not contented

This leaves (36 - 11 - 3 - 6) = 16 contented cows which are not fat and are not Jerseys,

and (20 - 11 - 3 - 2) = 4 fat cows which are not contented and not Jerseys,

and (27 - 11 - 6 - 2) = 8 Jersey cows which are neither fat nor contented,

and (55 - 11 - 3 - 6 - 2 - 16 - 4 - 8) = 5 cows which are not contented, not fat and not Jerseys.

IN EACH OF THESE QUESTIONS, DRAW A VENN DIAGRAM
AND PLACE THE NUMBERS IN THE CORRECT REGIONS.
FOR QUESTIONS 1, 2, 3, 4 DRAW A DIAGRAM LIKE THE ONE ON
PAGE 28 **A**; FOR QUESTION 5 DRAW ONE LIKE 28 **B**.

a

1) ε = {people altogether}, I= {Indians}, W= {women}

9 people were Indian women

7 people were Indians but not women

14 people were women but not Indians

18 people were neither Indians nor women

(a) How many Indians were there altogether?

(b) How many people were there altogether?

2) ε = {boys}, P= {boys who played the piano},

R= {boys who played the recorder},

30 boys altogether, 11 played only the piano, 8 played both
piano and recorder, 7 played neither.

(a) How many played only the recorder?

(b) How many altogether played the piano?

3) ε = {people}, H= {people wearing hats},

U= {people carrying umbrellas}

12 people wearing hats, 10 people carrying umbrellas,

7 people wearing hats and carrying umbrellas, 19 people
neither wearing hats nor carrying umbrellas.

(a) How many people altogether?

(b) How many people wearing hats but not carrying
umbrellas?

4) ε = {cars}, G= {green cars}, R= {cars fitted with radios}

30 cars, 11 were green cars fitted with radios, altogether 19
cars were fitted with radios, 4 green cars were not fitted with
radios

(a) How many cars were fitted with radios but were not green?

(b) How many cars without radios were not green?

5) ε = {girls}, T= {tall girls}, E= {English girls},

I= {intelligent girls}

38 girls, 20 are English, 11 are tall, 27 are intelligent, 4 are tall
intelligent English girls, 5 are tall and English but not intelligent,
10 are intelligent English girls who are not tall; 2 are tall but are not
English and not intelligent.

(a) How many girls are neither English nor intelligent?

(b) How many girls are not tall, not English and not intelligent?

(c) How many tall, intelligent non-English girls are there?

HOURS, MINUTES, SECONDS
A Fractions of an hour

1 minute $= \frac{1}{60}$ hour

2 minutes $= \frac{2}{60} = \frac{1}{30}$ hour, etc.

To convert minutes into fractions of an hour

e.g.　Express 35 minutes as a fraction of 1 hour

*1)　Divide by 60　　$\frac{35}{60}$

*2)　Cancel to lowest terms　　$\frac{35}{60} = \frac{7}{12}$ hour

e.g. (2) Express 4 hours 40 minutes as a number of hours

$$4\frac{40}{60} = 4\frac{40^{2}}{60_{3}} = 4\frac{2}{3} \text{ hours}$$

B To convert fractions of an hour into minutes

e.g. Convert $\frac{5}{6}$ hour into minutes

*1)　Multiply by 60　　$\frac{5}{6} \times \frac{60}{1}$

*2)　Cancel as far as you can　　$\frac{5}{6} \times \frac{60^{10}}{1} = 50$ minutes

e.g. (2) What is $2\frac{4}{5}$ hours in hours and minutes?

$$2\frac{4}{5} \text{ hours} = 2 \text{ hours} \quad \frac{4}{5} \times \frac{60^{12}}{1} \text{ minutes}$$

$$= 2 \text{ hours } 48 \text{ minutes}$$

C

60 minutes = 1 hour	60 min = 1 h
60 seconds = 1 minute	60 s = 1 min
3600 seconds = 1 hour	3600 s = 1 h

Conversion

hours to minutes	× 60
minutes to hours	÷ 60
minutes to seconds	× 60
seconds to minutes	÷ 60
hours to seconds	× 3600
seconds to hours	÷ 3600

e.g. Express 11 minutes in seconds　$11 \times 60 = 660$ seconds

a
Express each of these as a fraction of 1 hour in its lowest terms

1) 12 minutes	6) 25 minutes	11) 13 minutes
2) 55 minutes	7) 3 minutes	12) 40 minutes
3) 30 minutes	8) 24 minutes	13) 15 minutes
4) 8 minutes	9) 45 minutes	14) 10 minutes
5) 20 minutes	10) 33 minutes	15) 54 minutes

b
Express each of these in **hours and fractions of an hour**

1) 3h 50min	6) 10h 35min	11) 5h 30min
2) 1h 16min	7) 1h 20min	12) 8h 6min
3) 5h 42 min	8) 7h 48min	13) 9h 44min
4) 6h 4 min	9) 2h 5min	14) 12h 40 min
5) 2h 45 min	10) 3h 40min	15) 4h 32 min

c
Express each of these in minutes

1) $\frac{1}{4}$ hour	6) $\frac{41}{60}$ hour	11) $\frac{9}{10}$ hour
2) $\frac{7}{12}$ hour	7) $\frac{2}{3}$ hour	12) $\frac{1}{12}$ hour
3) $\frac{4}{5}$ hour	8) $\frac{1}{6}$ hour	13) $\frac{17}{20}$ hour
4) $\frac{3}{10}$ hour	9) $\frac{11}{12}$ hour	14) $\frac{7}{60}$ hour
5) $\frac{1}{2}$ hour	10) $\frac{1}{3}$ hour	15) $\frac{13}{15}$ hour

d
Express each of these in **hours and minutes**

e.g.   5¼ hours = 5 hours 15 minutes

1) $3\frac{3}{4}$ hours	6) $5\frac{5}{6}$ hours	11) $10\frac{2}{3}$ hours
2) $2\frac{1}{3}$ hours	7) $2\frac{7}{10}$ hours	12) $8\frac{1}{2}$ hours
3) $6\frac{7}{12}$ hours	8) $7\frac{3}{5}$ hours	13) $3\frac{1}{6}$ hours
4) $4\frac{1}{4}$ hours	9) $4\frac{11}{20}$ hours	14) $5\frac{4}{15}$ hours
5) $1\frac{31}{60}$ hours	10) $1\frac{7}{15}$ hours	15) $1\frac{4}{5}$ hours

e
1) Express as a number of minutes

   (a) 4 hours   (b) 9 hours   (c) 2¼ hours   (d) $3\frac{3}{10}$ hours
   (e) $1\frac{3}{5}$ hours

2) Express as a number of seconds

   (a) 7 minutes   (b) 3 minutes   (c) 1½ minutes
   (d) 5⅓ minutes   (e) ¾ hour

3) Express as a number of minutes

   (a) 120 seconds   (b) 200 seconds   (c) $4\frac{5}{6}$ hours
   (d) 65 seconds   (e) 395 seconds

4) Express as a number of hours

   (a) 480 minutes   (b) 210 minutes   (c) 340 minutes
   (d) 4200 seconds   (e) 175 minutes

A SPEED (1)

SPEED = DISTANCE ÷ TIME $\qquad S = \dfrac{D}{T}$

e.g. A ball, travelling at a steady speed, goes 100 metres in 5 seconds. What is its speed?

FIRST Write out values of DISTANCE and TIME $\qquad D = 100, T = 5$

THEN Work out speed $\quad S = \dfrac{100}{5} = 20$

Ball travels at 20 m/s

Note Speeds are always written in **distance per time** units, e.g. m/s (metres per second), miles/h (miles per hour), etc.

B Uniform speed and average speed

Things which travel at the same speed all the time have a UNIFORM SPEED (or STEADY SPEED).

Most things which move in the real world (trains, people, aeroplanes, tennis balls, spiders, etc.) do NOT travel at uniform speed, but you can still find their AVERAGE SPEED by the same formula.

$$S = \frac{D}{T}$$

e.g. A train went 380 miles in 5 hours. What was its average speed?

$$D = 380 \quad , \quad T = 5$$

$$S = \frac{380}{5} = 76$$

Average speed of the train was 76 miles/h

C Hours and minutes

Always express hours and minutes in HOURS AND FRACTIONS OF AN HOUR (unless the question asks you to work in minutes). Look at page 30 A if you are not sure.

e.g. What is the average speed of a car which travels 132 miles in 2h 45min?

$$D = 132, \quad T = 2\tfrac{3}{4}$$

$$S = 132 \div 2\tfrac{3}{4} = \frac{132}{1} \div \frac{11}{4} = 48 \text{ miles/h}$$

a Find the speed (S) from each distance (D) and time (T)

1) D = 35 m, T = 5 s
2) D = 630 miles, T = 7 h
3) D = 48 km, T = 3 h
4) D = 8 m, T = 0.2 s
5) D = 64.5 m, T = 5 min
6) D = 506 miles, T = 22 h
7) D = 65 km, T = 2½ h
8) D = 49 m, T = 3½ s
9) D = 405 miles, T = 13½ h
10) D = 5340 km, T = 12 h

---

b Find the average speed of

1) a boy who walks 27 miles in 9 hours
2) a boat which travels 84 km in 6 hours
3) a cricket ball which travels 138 metres in 6 seconds
4) a girl who cycles 72 miles in 4½ hours
5) an aeroplane which flies 1008 miles in 5¼ hours
6) a snail which goes 4 metres in 8 minutes
7) a yacht which sails 12 miles in 1⅓ hours
8) a bee which flies 44 metres in 8 seconds
9) a locomotive which travels 208 miles in 2⅔ hours
10) an athlete who runs 400 metres in 64 seconds

---

c Find the average speed of

1) an airliner which travels 910 miles in 2 hours 30 minutes
2) a car which travels 105 miles in 2 hours 20 minutes
3) a boy who walks 13½ miles in 3 h 45 min
4) a train which travels 490 miles in 5 h 50 min
5) a ship which goes 88 km in 3 h 40 min
6) a man who cycles 31½ miles in 2 h 15 min
7) a train which goes 400 miles in 4 h 10 min
8) a pigeon which flies 137½ km in 2 h 5 min
9) a helicopter which sets off at 13 15 and travels 120 miles, ending its journey at 14 55
10) a bus which departs from Spalding at 18 45 and arrives at Melton Mowbray, 36 miles away, at 20 21

A SPEED (2)
Finding DISTANCE

DISTANCE = SPEED × TIME   D = ST

e.g. A car travels for 5 hours at a speed of 38 miles/hour.
How far does it travel ?

S = 38
T = 5   D = 38 × 5 = 190 miles

e.g. (2) An aeroplane flies at a speed of 474 km/h for 3 hours
10 minutes. How far does it fly?

S = 474
$T = 3\frac{1}{6}$ $D = 474 \times 3\frac{1}{6} = \frac{474}{1} \times \frac{19}{6}$ = 1501 km

---

B Finding TIME

TIME = DISTANCE ÷ SPEED $T = \frac{D}{S}$

e.g. A bird flew a distance of 105 miles at an average speed of
15 miles/h. How long did its journey take?

D = 105
S = 15 $T = \frac{105}{15}$ = 7 hours

e.g. (2) A train travelled from Darlington to London, a distance of
232 miles, at an average speed of 80 miles/h. How long, in hours
and minutes, did it take?

D = 232
S = 80

$T = \frac{232}{80} = \frac{29}{10}$ = $2\frac{9}{10}$ hours
= 2 hours ($\frac{9}{10} \times \frac{60}{1}$) minutes
= 2 hours 54 minutes

REMEMBER To change a fraction of an hour into minutes,
multiply by 60 (see page 30 B).

C

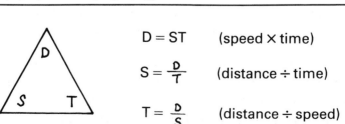

D = ST   (speed × time)

$S = \frac{D}{T}$ (distance ÷ time)

$T = \frac{D}{S}$ (distance ÷ speed)

a ALWAYS READ THE QUESTION CAREFULLY AND MAKE SURE
WHAT YOU HAVE BEEN ASKED TO FIND. Is it SPEED,
or DISTANCE, or TIME?

1) Steven walked for 3 hours at an average speed of 5 km/h.
What distance did he walk?

2) A boy ran 200 metres at a speed of 5 m/s. How long did it take him?

3) Barbara cycled at an average speed of 13 miles/h. If her
journey took 2½ hours, how far did she go?

4) A golf ball travelled a distance of 27 m at a speed of 36 m/s.
How long did it take?

5) An aircraft flew 880 miles at a speed of 330 miles/h. How long,
in hours and minutes, did its journey take?

6) A train travels for 4 h 45 min at an average speed of 84 miles/h.
Calculate the distance it travels.

7) Bert drove his truck from Exeter to Manchester a distance of 240
miles, in 5 hours 20 minutes. What was his average speed?

8) Kathy and Sara went on a 16½ mile hike. Their average
walking speed was 2¾ miles/h. How long did it take them?

9) Light travels at about 186000 mile/s. The sun is about
93 000 000 miles from Earth. About how many seconds does it
take sunlight to reach the Earth?

10) A motorist drove from Girvan to Edinburgh in 2 hours
40 minutes at an average speed of 34½ miles/h. Find the
distance from Girvan to Edinburgh.

11) Mohammed and his uncle travelled from Liverpool to
Nottingham, a distance of 99 miles, in 2 hours 45 minutes.
What was their average speed?

12) A snail, travelling at 13½ m/hour, went from the wheelbarrow
to the plastic gnome 5⅖ m away. How long, in minutes, did
its journey take?

13) A bottle containing a message was launched from St. Kilda
island on March 23 and reached Stromness, after floating
242 miles, on May 6. What was the average speed of the bottle
in miles/day?

14) Angela set off on her motorbike at 3.46 p.m. and rode at an
average speed of 48 miles/h until 4.21 p.m. By first finding how
long, in hours, she took, calculate how far she went.

15) A train leaves Glasgow at 08 20 and travels 88 miles to
Taynuilt at an average speed of 31³⁄₇ miles/h. At what time
does it reach Taynuilt?

A SPEED (3)
Average speed

$$\text{AVERAGE SPEED} = \frac{\text{Total distance}}{\text{Total time}}$$

e.g. (1) A man cycled a distance of 30 miles in $2\frac{1}{2}$ hours, then walked 6 miles in $1\frac{1}{2}$ hours. What was his average speed for the whole journey?

Total distance $= 30 + 6 = 36$ miles
Total time $= 2\frac{1}{2} + 1\frac{1}{2} = 4$ hours

$$\text{Average speed} = \frac{36}{4} = \underline{9 \text{ miles/hour}}$$

---

e.g. (2) Karen walked $7\frac{1}{2}$ miles in 2 hours 10 minutes. Then she travelled a further $6\frac{1}{4}$ miles by bus. The bus took 20 minutes. Find her average speed for the whole journey.

Total distance $= 7\frac{1}{2} + 6\frac{1}{4} = 13\frac{3}{4}$ miles
Total time $= 2\,h\,10\,min + 20\,min = 2\,h\,30\,min = 2\frac{1}{2}$ hours

$$\text{Average speed} = \frac{13\frac{3}{4}}{2\frac{1}{2}} = 13\frac{3}{4} \div 2\frac{1}{2} = \frac{55}{4} \div \frac{5}{2}$$
$$= \frac{^{11}55}{4_2} \times \frac{2^1}{5_1} = \underline{5\frac{1}{2} \text{ miles/hour}}$$

---

e.g. (3) James travelled on a train for 2 hours 10 minutes at an average speed of 66 miles/hour. Then he went by taxi for 30 minutes at an average speed of 34 miles/hour. By finding the total distance he travelled, calculate his average speed for the whole journey.

<u>Train</u>   Distance = Speed × Time $66 \times 2\frac{1}{6} = 143$ miles

<u>Taxi</u>   Distance = Speed × Time $34 \times \frac{1}{2} = 17$ miles

Total distance $= 143 + 17 = 160$ miles
Total time $= 2\frac{1}{6} + \frac{1}{2} = 2\frac{2}{3}$ miles

$$\text{Average speed} = 160 \div 2\frac{2}{3} = \underline{60 \text{ miles/hour}}$$

a

1) Paul ran 420m in 119 seconds and then walked 160m in 171 seconds. What was his average speed?

2) A car travelled 145 miles in 4 hours, then 83 miles in 2 hours. Find its average speed for the whole journey.

3) Naomi and Rachel left school at 1603 and walked to the bus stop, arriving there at 1619, just in time to catch the bus which took 32 minutes to reach their house. The distance from the school to their house was 12 miles. Find their average speed in miles/hour for the whole journey.

4) Edward cycled 31km in 1 hour 10 minutes. Then he walked 11km in 2 hours 20 minutes. Find his average speed for the whole journey.

5) A tennis ball travelled a distance of 61 metres through the air for 2½ seconds. Then it rolled 44m along the ground for 5 seconds. Calculate its average speed.

6) Christine travelled 39 miles by train. The journey took 55 minutes. She then went by car for another 9 miles, taking a further 17 minutes. What was her average speed, in miles/hour, for the complete journey?

7) An aeroplane made a journey in two stages. The first stage, at an average speed of 324km/h, was completed in 40 minutes. The second stage, at an average speed of 296km/h, was completed in 30 minutes. What was its average speed for the whole journey?

8) A bus went from Salisbury to Exeter. It travelled for 1h 10min at an average speed of 27 miles/h. Then it travelled for 25min at an average speed of 42 miles/h. By finding both distances, calculate the total distance from Salisbury to Exeter.

9) A train travelled for 1h 15min at 76 miles/h, and then for 45min at 84 miles/h. Find the two distances the train travelled and from your answers calculate the average speed of the train for the complete journey.

10) Adrian travelled from Cambridge to London, a distance of 55 miles, at an average speed of 60 miles/hour. He returned to Cambridge at an average speed of 30 miles/hour. What was his average speed from Cambridge to London and back?

SPEED (4)
A Conversions

e.g. Express a speed of 20m/s in km/h

> 3600 seconds = 1 hour
> 1000 metres = 1 kilometre

In 1 second the distance covered is 20 metres, so in 1 hour the distance covered is $20 \times 3600 = 72000$ metres

$$72000 \text{ metres} = \frac{72\,000}{1000} = 72 \text{ kilometres}$$

so a speed of 20 m/s = __72 km/h__

---

e.g. (2) An airliner travels at a speed of 576 km/h. What is its speed in metres/second?

> 1000 metres = 1 kilometre
> 3600 seconds = 1 hour

In 1 hour it travels $576 \times 1000 = 576\,000$ m

so in 1 second it travels $\frac{576\,000}{3600} = 160$ m

Airliner's speed is __160 metres/second__

---

e.g. (3) Express 4.2 m/min in cm/sec

> 100 centimetres = 1 metre
> 60 seconds = 1 minute

4.2 m/min

$= 4.2 \times 100 = 420 \text{ cm/min} = \frac{420}{60}$

$= \underline{7 \text{ cm/sec}}$

---

e.g. (4) Express 2.25 cm/s in km/h

> 3600 seconds = 1 hour
> 100 000 centimetres = 1 kilometre

$2.25 \text{ cm/s} = 2.25 \times 3600 = 8100 \text{ cm/h}$

$= \frac{8100}{100\,000}$

$= \underline{0.081 \text{ km/h}}$

a A man walked at 2 metres/second.
1) How many metres did he walk in an hour?
2) How many kilometres did he walk in an hour?
3) What was his speed in kilometres/hour?

A train travelled at 108 kilometres/hour.
4) How many metres did it travel in an hour?
5) What was its speed in metres/second?

b Express in km/h
1) 5 m/s
2) 12 m/s
3) 40 m/s
4) 0.25 m/s
5) 100 m/s
6) 45 m/s
7) 1⅔ m/s
8) 9⅙ m/s
9) 18.5 m/s
10) N m/s

c Express in m/s
1) 36 km/h
2) 4½ km/h
3) 126 km/h
4) 1080 km/h
5) 2.7 km/h
6) 63 km/h
7) 66600 km/h
8) ⅘ km/h
9) 414 km/h
10) Y km/h

d By multiplying and/or dividing by the correct amounts, do these conversions.
1) Express 27 m/min in cm/s
2) Express 9 km/h in m/min
3) Write 219 m/min in cm/s
4) Express 55 m/s in km/hour
5) Write 70 cm/s in m/min
6) An aeroplane travelled at 486 km/h. What was its speed in m/s?
7) A boy walked at 5.4 km/h. Express his speed in cm/s
8) Sound travels through air at about 330 m/s. Express this speed in km/h
9) A sailing ship travelled at 450 metres/minute. What was its speed in km/h?
10) What is the speed in m/min of a giraffe which runs at 39 km/h?

cm = centimetres	m = metres
h = hours	min = minutes
km = kilometres	s = seconds

A OTHER BASES (1)

Normal counting is done in **BASE 10** (also called DENARY or DECIMAL), i.e.

1, 2, 3, 4, 5, 6, 7, 8, 9, 10, 11, 12, 13, etc.

In BASE 10, TEN different figures (or digits) are used, i.e. 0,1,2,3,4,5,6,7,8 and 9

Counting in other bases can be just as easy
e.g. In **BASE 6**, six different figures are used

0, 1, 2, 3, 4 and 5

In BASE 6, no figure larger than 5 may be used, so counting in base 6 goes

1, 2, 3, 4, 5, 10, 11, 12, 13, 14, 15, 20, etc

e.g. In **BASE 2** (binary), two different figures are used

0, 1

In base 2 (binary) no figure larger than 1 may be used, so counting in base 2 goes

1, 10, 11, 100, 101, 110, 111, 1000, 1001, 1010, 1011, etc.

Base 2 is usually called BINARY
Base 3 is sometimes called TERNARY
Base 8 is sometimes called OCTAL

NOTE Bases can be larger than 10, e.g. base 16 (hexadecimal, but usually called just HEX), which is used in computing.
For bases larger than 10, new 'figures' must be invented,
e.g. counting in base 16 goes 1, 2, 3, 4, 5, 6, 7, 8, 9, A, B, C, D, E, F, 10, 11, etc.

B Columns in other bases

The columns in ordinary counting (base 10) are

<u>10000</u> <u>1000</u> <u>100</u> <u>10</u> <u>1</u>

Each column is multiplied by <u>10</u> to get the next bigger column.
In other bases each column is multiplied BY THE BASE to get the next column, e.g. in base 4

$$4^4 \qquad 4^3 \qquad 4^2 \qquad 4^1 \qquad 4^0$$
$$(64 \times 4)\ (16 \times 4)\ (4 \times 4)\ (1 \times 4)$$
$$\underline{256} \qquad \underline{64} \qquad \underline{16} \qquad \underline{4} \qquad \underline{1} \qquad \text{etc.}$$

IMPORTANT. The right-hand column is always the UNITS COLUMN (the ONES column) in any base.

a e.g. Write down the first fifteen numbers in base 5, starting with 1
Answer 1,2,3,4,10,11,12,13,14,20,21,22,23,24,30

Write down, starting with 1,
1) the first ten numbers in base 3
2) the first twenty numbers in base 8
3) the first ten numbers in base 4
4) the first fifteen numbers in base 7
5) the first twenty numbers in base 9

---

b e.g. Find the next five consecutive numbers above 14 in base 7
Answer 15, 16, 20, 21, 22
1) Find the next four consecutive numbers above 26 in base 8
2) Find the next five consecutive numbers above 1212 in base 3
3) Find the next three consecutive numbers below 61 in base 7
4) Find the next four consecutive numbers above 42 in base 5
5) Find the next four consecutive numbers below 122 in base 6

---

c e.g. Find the values of $7^3, 7^2, 7^1, 7^0$, and set them out as columns in base 7
$7^3 = 7 \times 7 \times 7 = 343$; $7^2 = 7 \times 7 = 49$; $7^1 = 7$; $7^0 = 1$
so answer is   **343**   **49**   **7**   **1**
REMEMBER. Anything to the power 0 = 1
e.g. $4^0 = 1$, $8^0 = 1$, etc.
In each of these, find the values of the numbers and set out the answers in columns

1) $8^3, 8^2, 8^1, 8^0$ 4) $10^5, 10^4, 10^3, 10^2, 10^1, 10^0$
2) $3^6, 3^5, 3^4, 3^3, 3^2, 3^1, 3^0$ 5) $12^2, 12^1, 12^0$
3) $2^7, 2^6, 2^5, 2^4, 2^3, 2^2, 2^1, 2^0$

---

d e.g. Work out the first five columns in base 3
Answer   **81**   **27**   **9**   **3**   **1**
Work out the first five columns in
1) base 6   4) base 7
2) base 4   5) base 5
3) base 9

A OTHER BASES (2)

The base of a number is written at the bottom after the number

e.g.   213 in base 5 is written 213_5

1011001 in binary is written 1011001_2

48 in base 10 (ordinary counting) is written 48_{10}

B Converting TO denary

To convert an 'other base' number into a denary (ordinary) number, e.g. Convert 1232_4 into denary

*1) Write the columns of the other base   **64   16   4   1**

*2) Place numbers in correct columns   1   2   3   2

(Remember. The right hand figure is always the UNITS)

*3) Work out each column $1 \times 64 = 64$

$2 \times 16 = 32$

$3 \times \ 4 = 12$

$2 \times \ 1 = \ 2$

*4) Add all the answers $64 + 32 + 12 + 2 = 110$

so $1232_4 \ = \ 110_{10}$

Other examples

1) Convert 76_8 into denary

$$\underline{8} \quad \underline{1}$$
$$7 \quad \ 6$$

$7 \times 8 = 56$

$6 \times 1 = \underline{\ 6} +$

62_{10}

---

2) Convert 1243_5 to base 10

$$\underline{125} \quad \underline{25} \quad \underline{5} \quad \underline{1}$$
$$1 \quad \ \ 2 \quad \ 4 \quad \ 3$$

$1 \times 125 = 125$

$2 \times \ \ 25 = \ \ 50$

$4 \times \ \ \ 5 = \ \ 20$

$3 \times \ \ \ 1 = \underline{\ \ \ 3} +$

198_{10}

3) Convert 101101_2 to denary

$$\underline{32} \quad \underline{16} \quad \underline{8} \quad \underline{4} \quad \underline{2} \quad \underline{1}$$
$$1 \quad \ \ 0 \quad \ 1 \quad 1 \quad 0 \quad 1$$

$1 \times 32 = 32$

$0 \times 16 = \ \ 0$

$1 \times \ \ 8 = \ \ 8$

$1 \times \ \ 4 = \ \ 4$

$0 \times \ \ 2 = \ \ 0$

$1 \times \ \ 1 = \underline{\ \ 1} +$

45_{10}

a
Write in short

e.g. 517 in base 9 = 517_9

1) 1010 in base 3
2) 62 in base 8
3) 345 in base 10
4) 1232 in base 5
5) 523 in base 7

6) 41 in base 9
7) 987 in base 11
8) 110111 in binary
9) 223 in base 4
10) 722 in octal

b
Convert each of these base 8 numbers to denary (base 10)

1) 31_8
2) 54_8
3) 65_8
4) 143_8

5) 77_8
6) 306_8
7) 222_8
8) 460_8

9) 1115_8
10) 544_8

c
Express these binary (base 2) numbers in denary (base 10)

1) 101_2
2) 1110_2
3) 1001_2
4) 11011_2
5) 10010_2

6) 111001_2
7) 11111_2
8) 101010_2
9) 11100_2
10) 1000000_2

d
Convert these numbers into denary

1) 13_6
2) 42_8
3) 24_5
4) 57_9
5) 1230_4

6) 121_3
7) 56_7
8) 102_5
9) 223_6
10) 212_4

11) 163_7
12) 1202_3
13) 142_9
14) 11101_2
15) 255_6

16) 86_9
17) 131_4
18) 267_8
19) 2211_3
20) 324_6

e
Express in denary

1) 111_7
2) 484_9
3) 1230_5
4) 20221_3
5) 2123_4

6) 523_8
7) 68_{11}
8) 1101100_2
9) 1433_6
10) 2411_5

11) 1432_8
12) 12121_3
13) 94_{13}
14) 246_9
15) 1000_6

16) 3032_4
17) 514_7
18) 100111_2
19) 636_8
20) 22020_3

OTHER BASES (3)

A Converting FROM denary

To convert an ordinary (denary, or base 10) number into an 'other base' number

e.g. Convert 73_{10} into base 6

*1) Divide the number by the base and write the remainder after the answer. Make sure there is a good gap between the answer and the remainder

```
6 | 73
  | 12      r.1
```

*2) Repeat until the answer is 0

```
6 | 73
6 | 12    r.1 ↑
6 |  2    r.0 |
  |  0    r.2 |
```

*3) Read the remainders from the bottom upwards

$$= 201_6$$

REMEMBER

1) There cannot be a remainder on the top line.
2) If there is no remainder, write 0
3) The **bottom remainder** is always the same figure as the **next-to-bottom answer**

e.g. Write 345_{10} as a number in base 5

```
5 | 345
5 |  69   0 ↑
5 |  13   4 |
5 |   2   3 |         = 2340₅
  |   0   2 |
```

$$= 2340_5$$

Other examples

1) Convert 77_{10} to binary

```
2 | 77
2 | 38   1 ↑
2 | 19   0 |
2 |  9   1 |
2 |  4   1 |
2 |  2   0 |
2 |  1   0 |
  |  0   1 |
```

$77_{10} = 1001101_2$

2) Express 171_{10} in base 8

```
8 | 171
8 |  21   3 ↑
8 |   2   5 |
  |   0   2 |
```

$171_{10} = 253_8$

3) Write the denary number 86 as a number in base 3

```
3 | 86
3 | 28   2 ↑
3 |  9   1 |
3 |  3   0 |
3 |  1   0 |
  |  0   1 |
```

$86_{10} = 10012_3$

a Write these denary numbers in base 5

1) 23_{10} 3) 49_{10} 5) 57_{10} 7) 78_{10} 9) 115_{10}
2) 66_{10} 4) 125_{10} 6) 6_{10} 8) 196_{10} 10) 1276_{10}

b Write these denary numbers in base 8

1) 38_{10} 3) 58_{10} 5) 95_{10} 7) 973_{10} 9) 155_{10}
2) 107_{10} 4) 136_{10} 6) 338_{10} 8) 52_{10} 10) 513_{10}

c Express these denary numbers in binary (base 2)

1) 7_{10} 6) 44_{10} 11) 21_{10} 16) 72_{10}
2) 36_{10} 7) 80_{10} 12) 100_{10} 17) 29_{10}
3) 24_{10} 8) 63_{10} 13) 55_{10} 18) 49_{10}
4) 11_{10} 9) 9_{10} 14) 16_{10} 19) 18_{10}
5) 39_{10} 10) 128_{10} 15) 5_{10} 20) 31_{10}

d Write

1) 28_{10} in base 6
2) 141_{10} in base 9
3) 55_{10} in base 3
4) 99_{10} in base 7
5) 47_{10} in base 2
6) 321_{10} in base 9
7) 73_{10} in base 4
8) 118_{10} in base 6
9) 277_{10} in base 5
10) 115_{10} in base 8
11) 89_{10} in base 3
12) 233_{10} in base 8
13) 44_{10} in base 5
14) 285_{10} in base 7
15) 39_{10} in base 4

e

For converting **other bases into denary (base 10)**, see page 42 B
For converting **denary (base 10) into other bases**, see page 44 A

1) 212_{10} to base 5
2) 191_{10} to base 7
3) 2100_3 to denary
4) 62_{10} to base 4
5) 3313_4 to base 10
6) 402_6 to denary
7) 91_{10} to base 2
8) 432_5 to denary
9) 606_{10} to base 9
10) 101110_2 to base 10
11) 350_9 to denary
12) 479_{10} to base 6
13) 111_{10} to base 3
14) 623_7 to base 10
15) 340_{10} to base 8

A OTHER BASES (4) +ADDITION

If no 'carrying' is needed, do just like a normal (base 10)

addition   e.g. 124_6

$\qquad\quad +230_6$

$\qquad\quad \overline{354_6}$

B 'Carrying'

HOW MANY GROUPS AND HOW MANY LEFT OVER?

e.g.   Add in BASE 7   : $236_7 + 154_7$

*How many groups of 7 and how many
left over? $6 + 4 = \mathbf{10}$ which is
1 group of 7 with 3 left over.

$\qquad\qquad$ Write down 3 and 'carry' 1

$$\begin{array}{ccc} 2 & 3 & 6 \\ + 1 & 5 & 4 \\ \hline & & 3 \end{array}$$

*How many groups of 7 and how many
left over? $3 + 5 + 1 = \mathbf{9}$ which is
1 group of 7 with 2 left over.

$\qquad\qquad$ Write down 2 and 'carry' 1

$$\begin{array}{ccc} 2 & 3 & 6 \\ + 1 & 5 & 4 \\ \hline & 2 & 3 \end{array}$$

$$\begin{array}{ccc} 2 & 3 & 6 \\ + 1 & 5 & 4 \\ \hline 4 & 2 & 3 \end{array}_7$$

Answer

---

e.g.   Add in BASE 8

$$\begin{array}{ccc} 7 & 6 & 5 \\ 2 & 4 & 7 \\ & 6 & 2 \\ \hline & & 6 \end{array}$$

1 group of 8 with 6 left over

$$\begin{array}{ccc} 7 & 6 & 5 \\ 2 & 4 & 7 \\ & 6 & 2 \\ \hline & 1 & 6 \end{array}$$

2 groups of 8 with 1 left over

$$\begin{array}{ccc} 7 & 6 & 5 \\ 2 & 4 & 7 \\ & 6 & 2 \\ \hline 3 & 1 & 6 \end{array}$$

1 group of 8 with 3 left over

Answer 1316_8

---

e.g. $2124_5 + 1243_5 + 104_5$

$$\begin{array}{cccc} 2 & 1 & 2 & 4 \\ 1 & 2 & 4 & 3 \\ & 1 & 0 & 4 \\ \hline & & & 1 \end{array}$$

2 groups of 5 with 1 left over

$$\begin{array}{cccc} 2 & 1 & 2 & 4 \\ 1 & 2 & 4 & 3 \\ & 1 & 0 & 4 \\ \hline & & 3 & 1 \end{array}$$

1 group of 5 with 3 left over

$$\begin{array}{cccc} 2 & 1 & 2 & 4 \\ 1 & 2 & 4 & 3 \\ & 1 & 0 & 4 \\ \hline & 0 & 3 & 1 \end{array}$$

1 group of 5 with 0 left over

$$\begin{array}{cccc} 2 & 1 & 2 & 4 \\ 1 & 2 & 4 & 3 \\ + & 1 & 0 & 4 \\ \hline 4 & 0 & 3 & 1 \end{array}_5$$

Answer

a Try these additions in base 8

1) 532_8	3) 25_8	5) 626_8	7) 135_8	9) 540_8
$+213_8$	$+364_8$	$+503_8$	$+542_8$	$+456_8$

2) 634_8	4) 743_8	6) 35_8	8) 5326_8	10) 446_8
$+\ 53_8$	$+\ 61_8$	24_8	$+\ 737_8$	545_8
		$+23_8$		$+612_8$

---

b
1) Add in base 7 : $514_7 + 634_7$
2) Add in base 3 : $1201_3 + 2102_3 + 221_3$
3) Add in base 5 : $314_5 + 240_5$
4) Add in base 9 : $13_9 + 562_9 + 438_9$
5) Add in base 4 : $123_4 + 201_4 + 22_4$

---

c
1) Add 713_8, 56_8, 101_8
2) Add 5232_6, 504_6
3) Add 1676_{10}, 835_{10}, 2131_{10}
4) Add 22_7, 1520_7, 413_7
5) Find the sum of 10101_3, 2012_3, 11212_3

---

d Try these additions

1) $242_5 + 134_5$
2) $1123_4 + 332_4$
3) $462_9 + 813_9 + 76_9$
4) $1452_6 + 3134_6$
5) $10011_2 + 110_2 + 1011_2$

6) $63_8 + 1620_8 + 377_8$
7) $53_6 + 44_6 + 25_6 + 32_6$
8) $501_7 + 342_7 + 64_7$
9) $975_{11} + 287_{11}$
10) $20_3 + 1120_3 + 212_3$

---

e
1) $663_7 + 4425_7$
2) $516_8 + 2032_8 + 621_8$
3) $210_3 + 112_3 + 212_3$
4) $330_6 + 52_6 + 1413_6$
5) $16_9 + 53_9 + 7_9 + 72_9$
6) $3402_5 + 2131_5 + 1234_5$
7) $853_{12} + 74_{12} + 708_{12}$
8) $1002_4 + 1133_4 + 321_4$

9) $64_8 + 26_8 + 35_8$
10) $302_5 + 130_5 + 3213_5$
11) $67_9 + 75_9 + 82_9$
12) $1101_2 + 111_2 + 10111_2$
13) $703_{10} + 48_{10} + 189_{10}$
14) $202_4 + 33_4 + 21_4$
15) $425_6 + 433_6$

48

OTHER BASES (5) —SUBTRACTION

A If no 'borrowing' is needed, do just like a normal (base 10) subtraction, e.g.

$$546_8$$
$$-204_8$$
$$\overline{342_8}$$

B 'Borrowing'

Borrow ONE GROUP from the next column
e.g.   Subtract in BASE 6 : $42_6 - 15_6$
*2 subtract 5 is not possible,
so 'borrow' a group of 6 from the
next column. Now instead of '2 subtract 5'
you have '8 subtract 5'

e.g.   Subtract 156_7 from 324_7

*4 subtract 6 is not possible, so
'borrow' a group of 7 from the
next column. Now you have '11 subtract 6'

*1 subtract 5 is not possible, so
'borrow' a group of 7 from the
next column. Now you have '8 subtract 5'

C MIXED ADDITION AND SUBTRACTION

*Do each stage separately
e.g. $1212_3 + 221_3 - 2101_3$

(a)
```
  1' 2' 1' 2
+    2 2 1
-----------
  2 2 1 0
```

(b)
```
  2 2 1 0
- 2 1 0 1
---------
    1 0 2₃
```

a Try these subtractions in base 5

1) 432_5	4) 42_5	7) 1242_5	10) 1101_5
-212_5	-23_5	-423_5	-324_5

2) 313_5	5) 240_5	8) 303_5
-122_5	-12_5	-34_5

3) 421_5	6) 331_5	9) 30_5
-33_5	-143_5	-12_5

b Subtract in base 7

1) $625_7 - 113_7$
2) $434_7 - 216_7$
3) $305_7 - 252_7$
4) $542_7 - 66_7$
5) $24_7 - 5_7$

6) $1305_7 - 561_7$
7) $614_7 - 132_7$
8) $1160_7 - 524_7$
9) $512_7 - 443_7$
10) $1502_7 - 415_7$

c
1) $313_4 - 120_4$
2) $741_9 - 274_9$
3) $1321_5 - 341_5$
4) $5216_8 - 2142_8$
5) $2021_3 - 212_3$

6) $420_6 - 53_6$
7) $11101_2 - 1010_2$
8) $40_5 - 12_5$
9) $4110_8 - 1372_8$
10) $82_9 - 7_9$

d
1) Find the difference between 2623_8 and 747_8
2) Subtract 4432_7 from 5000_7
3) Find the difference between 6004_9 and 235_9
4) Subtract 1310_6 from 5425_6
5) Find the difference between 12021_3 and 1202_3

e
1) $132_4 + 1222_4$
2) $7101_8 - 465_8$
3) $2433_5 - 1144_5$
4) $1111_2 + 111_2 + 11_2$
5) $551_6 - 45_6$

6) $524_8 + 655_8 - 730_8$
7) $2211_3 - 1012_3 - 222_3$
8) $122_4 + 123_4 - 230_4$
9) $31_9 + 585_9 + 156_9$
10) $4131_5 - 1332_5 + 2201_5$

A OTHER BASES (6) ×MULTIPLICATION

This is like addition (see page 46)

'Carrying' HOW MANY GROUPS AND HOW MANY LEFT OVER?

e.g.   Multiply in BASE 4   : $1321_4 \times 3$

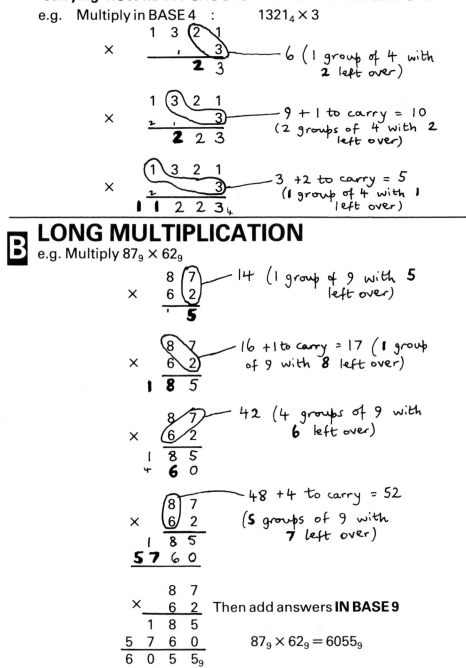

```
        1 3 (2  1
  ×        (    3
         1
          2  3              ── 6 ( 1 group of 4 with
                                      2 left over)

        1 (3  2  1
  ×         (    3
        2   1
           2  2  3          ── 9 + 1 to carry = 10
                               (2 groups of 4 with 2
                                         left over)

       (1  3  2  1
  ×              3
        2
      1  1  2  2  3₄        ── 3 +2 to carry = 5
                               (1 group of 4 with 1
                                         left over)
```

B LONG MULTIPLICATION

e.g. Multiply $87_9 \times 62_9$

```
        8 (7)                ── 14 (1 group of 9 with 5
  ×     6 (2)                             left over)
          1
            5

        (8  7)               ── 16 +1 to carry = 17 ( 1 group
  ×     6  (2)                   of 9 with 8 left over)
      1  8  5

        8  (7)               ── 42 (4 groups of 9 with
  ×    (6)  2                          6 left over)
      1  8  5
      4
        6  0

       (8) 7                 ── 48 +4 to carry = 52
  ×    (6) 2                    (5 groups of 9 with
      1  8  5                          7 left over)
    5  7  6  0
```

```
        8  7
  ×     6  2           Then add answers IN BASE 9
     1  8  5
   5  7  6  0              $87_9 \times 62_9 = 6055_9$
   6  0  5  5₉
```

a Multiply in base 7
1) 251_7 x 5   5) 361_7 x 2   9) 2012_7 x 3
2) 46_7 x 3   6) 2342_7 x 4   10) 513_7 x 5
3) 1043_7 x 6   7) 1241_7 x 3
4) 622_7 x 4   8) 605_7 x 6

b
1) 423_6 x 3   8) 235_8 x 4   15) 64_9 x 8
2) 2012_3 x 2   9) 221_3 x 2   16) 223_4 x 2
3) 576_8 x 6   10) 431_5 x 4   17) 1201_3 x 2
4) 322_4 x 3   11) 304_6 x 5   18) 1450_8 x 5
5) 1125_6 x 4   12) 27_8 x 7   19) 2317_9 x 5
6) 572_9 x 3   13) 1310_4 x 3   20) 142_5 x 3
7) 1323_5 x 2   14) 268_{11} x 9

c Do these by long multiplication
1) 34_5 x 23_5 6) 312_4 x 12_4
2) 37_8 x 43_8 7) 36_7 x 34_7
3) 120_3 x 11_3 8) 63_8 x 26_8
4) 251_6 x 14_6 9) 11010_2 x 11_2
5) 72_9 x 36_9 10) 42_6 x 52_6

d
1) 354_6 x 44_6 6) 430_5 x 41_5
2) 211_3 x 12_3 7) 115_8 x 36_8
3) 28_9 x 14_9 8) 32_4 x 31_4
4) 1010_2 x 101_2 9) 534_7 x 52_7
5) 64_7 x 24_7 10) 22_3 x 21_3

e
1) 123_4 x 3   6) 136_8 x 47_8
2) 5465_8 + 764_8 7) 2221_3 + 1202_3
3) 2121_3 x 22_3 8) 10110_2 − 1101_2
4) 503_7 − 346_7 9) 321_5 x 34_5
5) 35_6 + 454_6 + 125_6 10) 520_9 − 173_9

A OTHER BASES (7) ÷ DIVISION

Remainders are **GROUPS OF THE BASE** you are working in.

e.g.   Divide 424_5 by   3

$4 \div 3 = 1$, remainder 1 group of 5

This makes the next figure $2 + 5 = 7$

$7 \div 3 = 2$, remainder 1 group of 5

This makes the next figure $4 + 5 = 9$

$9 \div 3 = 3$

$= \underline{123_5}$

---

e.g. (2) $1426_8 \div 5$

$1 \div 5 = 0$, remainder
1 group of 8
making next figure $4 + 8 = 12$

$12 \div 5 = 2$, remainder
2 groups of 8
making next figure $2 + 8 + 8 = 18$

$18 \div 5 = 3$, remainder
3 groups of 8
making next figure $6 + 8 + 8 + 8 = 30$

$30 \div 5 = 6$

$= \underline{236_8}$

** ALL THE DIVISIONS ON THIS PAGE SHOULD **WORK OUT COM-PLETELY**. THERE SHOULD NOT BE ANY REMAINDERS IN THE FINAL ANSWERS.

a Do these divisions in base 6
REMEMBER. Each remainder in the working is **a group of 6**

1)	$532_6 \div 4$	5)	$350_6 \div 3$	8)	$510_6 \div 3$
2)	$1303_6 \div 3$	6)	$1344_6 \div 2$	9)	$1512_6 \div 2$
3)	$2124_6 \div 4$	7)	$253_6 \div 5$	10)	$224_6 \div 4$
4)	$221_6 \div 5$				

b Try these divisions in base 8

1)	$520_8 \div 4$	5)	$1452_8 \div 3$	8)	$3454_8 \div 6$
2)	$622_8 \div 6$	6)	$2104_8 \div 7$	9)	$473_8 \div 3$
3)	$1767_8 \div 5$	7)	$771_8 \div 5$	10)	$1674_8 \div 4$
4)	$712_8 \div 2$				

c

1)	$52_6 \div 4$	6)	$733_8 \div 5$	11)	$233_5 \div 4$
2)	$645_7 \div 3$	7)	$10021_3 \div 2$	12)	$664_7 \div 5$
3)	$2112_3 \div 2$	8)	$76_9 \div 3$	13)	$1210_4 \div 2$
4)	$33_5 \div 2$	9)	$330_4 \div 2$	14)	$840_9 \div 6$
5)	$66_7 \div 4$	10)	$1034_5 \div 3$	15)	$2431_6 \div 5$

d

1)	$2303_5 \div 4$	6)	$3424_5 \div 3$	11)	$3652_9 \div 4$
2)	$353_6 \div 3$	7)	$3201_4 \div 3$	12)	$1102_3 \div 2$
3)	$11211_3 \div 2$	8)	$283_{11} \div 9$	13)	$3134_8 \div 4$
4)	$2651_8 \div 7$	9)	$2343_7 \div 6$	14)	$651_{12} \div 5$
5)	$132_7 \div 4$	10)	$623_{10} \div 7$	15)	$10323_4 \div 3$

e

1)	$258_9 \div 5$	6)	$285_9 \times 7$	11)	$11021_3 - 110_3$
2)	$534_7 + 2136_7$	7)	$1641_7 \div 2$	12)	$2332_8 \div 6$
3)	$234_5 \div 3$	8)	$6013_8 - 54_8$	13)	$55_6 \times 5$
4)	$1312_4 \times 2$	9)	$233_4 \times 23_4$	14)	$331_4 + 23_4$
					$+ 302_4$
5)	$3210_4 - 323_4$	10)	$445_6 + 25_6$	15)	$2412_5 \div 3$

A OTHER BASES (8) — BINARY

BINARY (base 2) can often be easier if you THINK AND COUNT in binary.

Counting in binary goes:

1, 10, 11, 100, 101, 110, 111, 1000, 1001, etc.,

so $1 + 1 = 10$, $1 + 1 + 1 = 11$, $1 + 1 + 1 + 1 = 100$, etc.

B Addition

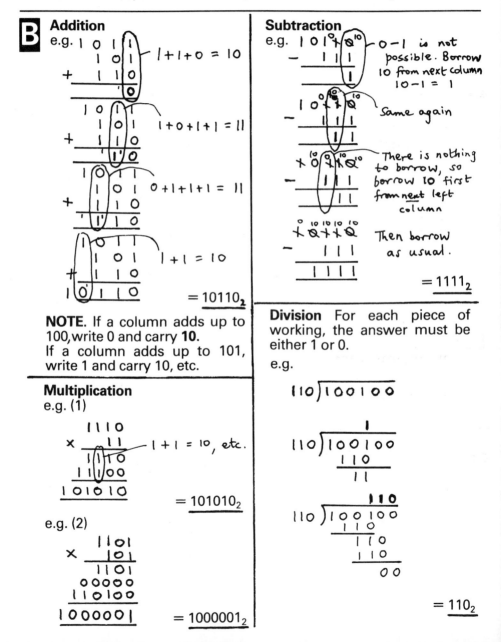

NOTE. If a column adds up to 100, write 0 and carry **10**.
If a column adds up to 101, write 1 and carry 10, etc.

Multiplication

e.g. (1)

$= 101010_2$

e.g. (2)

$= 1000001_2$

Subtraction

$0 - 1$ is not possible. Borrow 10 from next column $10 - 1 = 1$

Same again

There is nothing to borrow, so borrow 10 first from next left column

Then borrow as usual.

$= 1111_2$

Division

For each piece of working, the answer must be either 1 or 0.

e.g.

$= 110_2$

** ALL THE NUMBERS IN THESE QUESTIONS ARE IN BINARY (BASE 2)

a

1) 1001 + 10
2) 111 + 1010
3) 1101 + 110 + 100
4) 111 + 111
5) 10011 + 10111

6) 1011 + 111 + 10
7) 11011 + 1101 + 11
8) 1100 + 110 + 1010
9) 1010 + 101 + 1110
10) 1101 + 1100 + 111

b

1) 11110 − 1100
2) 1110 − 101
3) 10101 − 1010
4) 10010 − 100
5) 1001001 − 10110

6) 101010 − 1111
7) 1000 − 101
8) 110101 − 11000
9) 1000110 − 1101
10) 101101 − 11101

c

1) 110 × 11
2) 1011 × 10
3) 110 × 101
4) 1010 × 111
5) 11001 × 11

6) 11011 × 111
7) 10001 × 101
8) 1101 × 110
9) 1111 × 111
10) 1011 × 101 × 11

d

1) 11011 ÷ 11
2) 10010 ÷ 11
3) 1011010 ÷ 101
4) 11010 ÷ 10
5) 100011 ÷ 111

6) 101010 ÷ 11
7) 11110 ÷ 110
8) 11000 ÷ 11
9) 10111001 ÷ 101
10) 1000101 ÷ 11

e

1) 1110 + 111 + 10110
2) 10101 × 101
3) 101011 − 1101
4) 11100 × 110
5) 100111 ÷ 11
6) 10110 − 1011
7) 101010 + 10101 + 11
8) 1000010 ÷ 110
9) 110111 × 11
10) 11001 ÷ 101
11) 101110 + 11011 + 100110
12) 110011 − 1010
13) 101010 × 111
14) 11000 − 10101
15) 101111 + 11010 + 1010

A ANGLES (1) - Types and sizes

An ANGLE is the shape made when two straight lines meet at a point. The straight lines are called ARMS of the angle.

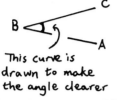

This curve is drawn to make the angle clearer

The drawing shows an angle.
This angle can be called ABC or CBA.
Angle ABC can be written in short
A$\hat{B}$C. The arms of this angle are AB
(or BA) and BC (or CB)

B

The size of an angle is usually measured in DEGREES (written ° for short).
These angles are marked with their sizes.

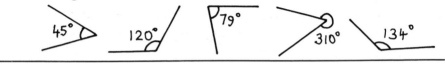

C

A **RIGHT ANGLE** is a square angle. Its size is 90 degrees (90°). It is usually marked ⌐ which means 90 degrees.

A **STRAIGHT ANGLE** is an angle of 180°

180°

A **REVOLUTION** is all the way round. Its size is 360°

D

An **ACUTE ANGLE** is an angle **more closed up than a right angle.** Its size is less than 90°

e.g.

An **OBTUSE ANGLE** is an angle **wider than a right angle but more closed up than a straight angle.** Its size is more than 90° but less than 180°

e.g.

A **REFLEX ANGLE** is an angle which turns back on itself. Its size is more than 180°.

e.g.

a Using a ruler, make a rough (but larger) copy of each angle. Then complete your copy by naming (a) the angle, and (b) its arms

e.g.

(a) Angle TUV
(b) Arms are TU and UV

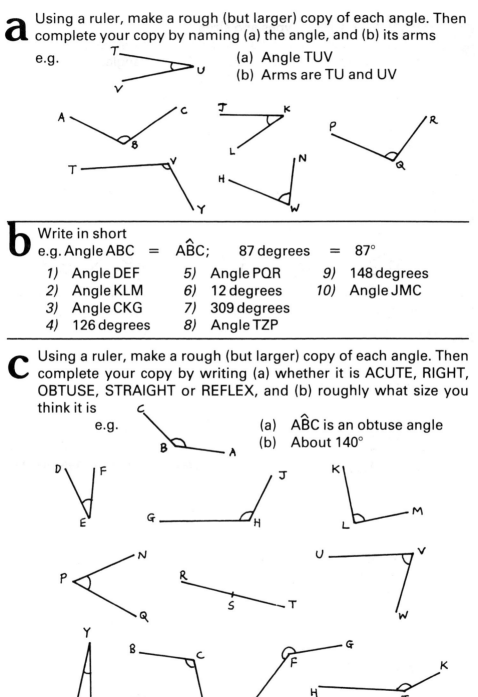

b Write in short

e.g. Angle ABC = AB̂C; 87 degrees = 87°

1) Angle DEF
2) Angle KLM
3) Angle CKG
4) 126 degrees
5) Angle PQR
6) 12 degrees
7) 309 degrees
8) Angle TZP
9) 148 degrees
10) Angle JMC

c Using a ruler, make a rough (but larger) copy of each angle. Then complete your copy by writing (a) whether it is ACUTE, RIGHT, OBTUSE, STRAIGHT or REFLEX, and (b) roughly what size you think it is

e.g.

(a) AB̂C is an obtuse angle
(b) About 140°

A ANGLES (2) - MEASURING ANGLES
Measuring angles with a protractor

FIRST Make a rough guess. How large is your angle compared with these?

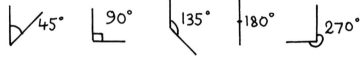

NEXT

*1) Find the **corner** of the angle. If the angle is called a three-letter name (e.g. AF̂H), the middle letter is the corner
*2) Place the protractor with the crossing lines on the corner of the angle
*3) Make the 0° line fit along one of the arms of the angle
*4) Look along the other arm of the angle and measure the size on the protractor
*5) **Check with your rough guess** to make sure you have read the angle correctly

---

B Clock face

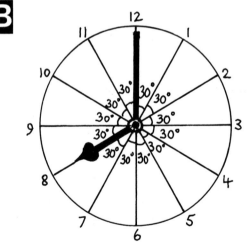

The angle between one number and the next is 30°

e.g. What is the (smaller) angle between the hands of a clock at 8 o'clock?

30 + 30 + 30 + 30

(**or** 4 x 30) = **120°**

The large hand is the **MINUTES** hand.
It moves through **360°** every hour.

The small hand is the **HOURS** hand.
It moves through **30°** every hour.

a

Measure each angle and write down its size
e.g.   t = 54°, $A\hat{B}C$ = 117°,   etc.

If the drawing is too small to measure properly, make an accurate tracing of the angle and extend (or produce) its arms. Then measure your tracing.

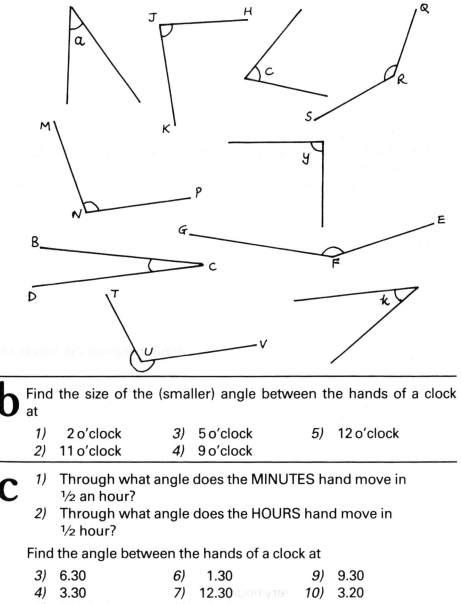

b

Find the size of the (smaller) angle between the hands of a clock at

1)   2 o'clock   3)   5 o'clock   5)   12 o'clock
2)   11 o'clock   4)   9 o'clock

c

1)   Through what angle does the MINUTES hand move in ½ an hour?
2)   Through what angle does the HOURS hand move in ½ hour?

Find the angle between the hands of a clock at

3)   6.30   6)   1.30   9)   9.30
4)   3.30   7)   12.30   10)   3.20
5)   7 o'clock   8)   4.30

ANGLES (3)

Angles in a REVOLUTION (all the way round a point) add up to 360°

e.g.

$55 + 92 + 86 + 66 + 61$

$= \mathbf{360°}$

Finding a missing angle

e.g. Find angle k

*1) Add all the other angles
$63 + 94 + 134 = 291$
*2) Subtract total from 360
$360 - 291 = 69$ k = 69°

e.g. (2) Find angle p

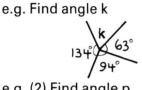

There are 5 angles p, all the same size

$$p = \frac{360}{5} = 72°$$

B Angles in a QUADRILATERAL add up to 360°

A quadrilateral is a four sided plane figure. Its INTERIOR angles (the angles inside it) add up to 360°

e.g.

$82 + 64 + 90 + 124 = 360°$

Finding a missing angle

e.g. Find angle JKL

*1) Add all the other angles
$41 + 58 + 135 = 234$
*2) Subtract total from 360
$360 - 234 = 126$
$J\hat{K}L = 126°$

e.g. (2) Find the size of angle w (Both the angles w are the same size)

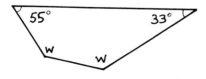

*1) Add the other angles
$55 + 33 = 88$
*2) Subtract total from 360
$360 - 88 = 272$
*3) Divide answer by 2
$$w = \frac{272}{2} = 136°$$

THESE ANGLES ARE NOT DRAWN TO SCALE. YOUR ANSWERS
SHOULD BE **CALCULATED**, NOT MEASURED WITH A
PROTRACTOR

a Find the size of each angle a, b, c, d, e

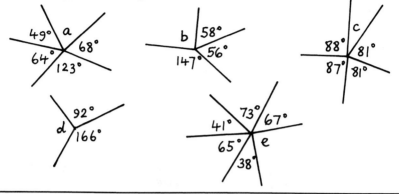

b Find the size of each angle f, g, h, j, k

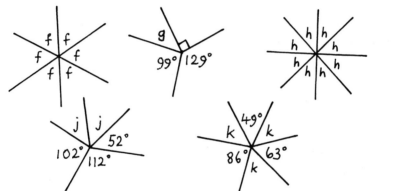

c Find the size of each angle l, m, n, p, q

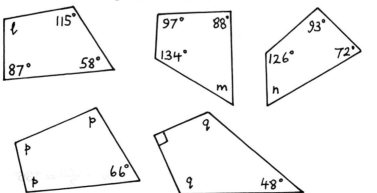

A ANGLES (4)

Angles on a STRAIGHT LINE add up to 180°

e.g.

48° 132°

48 + 132 = 180°

59° 86° 35°

59 + 86 + 35 = 180°

Finding a missing angle

e.g. Find angle QTR

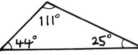

180 − 37 − 75 = 68

$\widehat{QTR}$ = 68°

B Angles in a TRIANGLE add up to 180°

A triangle is a three sided plane figure. Its INTERIOR angles (the angles inside it) add up to 180°

e.g.

111°

44° 25°

44 + 25 + 111 = 180°

Finding a missing angle

e.g. Calculate $\widehat{BCD}$

B 73°   C

80°
D

180 − 73 − 80 = 27°

C ISOSCELES TRIANGLE has two equal angles, and two equal sides

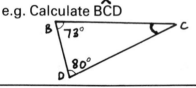

B

A 63°   C

The two sides AB and BC are equal in length. They are marked with the same sort of small lines to show that they are equal.

Angles BAC and BCA are equal

Find the sizes of angles BCA and ABC

1) $\widehat{BCA}$ = $\widehat{BAC}$ because triangle ABC is isosceles, with AB = BC, so $\widehat{BCA}$ = 63°

2) $\widehat{ABC}$ = 180 − 63 − 63 = 54°, because angles in a triangle add up to 180°

a THESE ANGLES ARE NOT DRAWN TO SCALE. YOUR ANSWERS SHOULD BE **CALCULATED,** NOT MEASURED WITH A PROTRACTOR

Find the size of each angle a, b, c, d, e

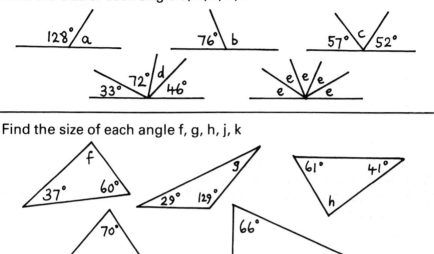

b Find the size of each angle f, g, h, j, k

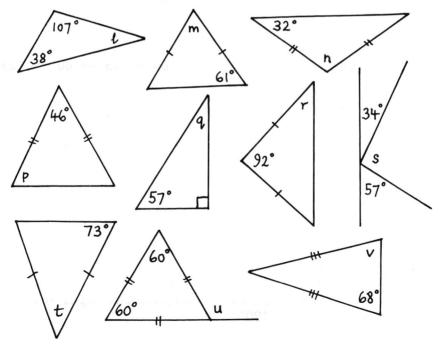

c Find the size of each angle l, m, n, p, q, r, s, t, u, v

ANGLES (5)

A VERTICALLY OPPOSITE ANGLES are equal

Vertically opposite angles are formed at the intersection of two straight lines. Vertically opposite angles are EQUAL

e.g.

B PARALLEL LINES

Parallel lines are pairs or groups of lines which stay the same distance apart.

Parallel lines are marked with the same kind of arrows to show that they are parallel

A line which crosses other lines is called a TRANSVERSAL

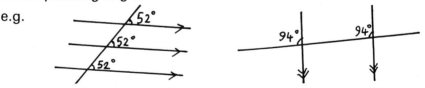

C CORRESPONDING ANGLES are equal

Angles in the same position on a set of parallel lines (between a transversal and a set of parallel lines) are called corresponding angles.

Corresponding angles are EQUAL

e.g.

D ALTERNATE ANGLES are equal

Angles on two (or more) parallel lines but at opposite sides of the transversal (angles in a Z shape) are called ALTERNATE ANGLES. Alternate angles are EQUAL

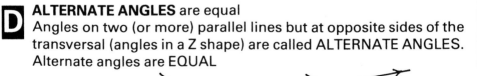
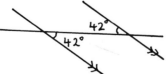
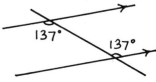

THESE ANGLES ARE NOT DRAWN TO SCALE. YOUR ANSWERS
SHOULD BE CALCULATED, NOT MEASURED WITH A
PROTRACTOR

a Find the size of each angle, a, b, c, d, e

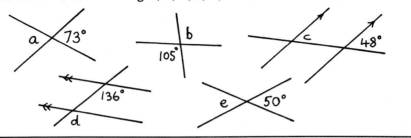

b Find the size of each angle f, g, h, j, k

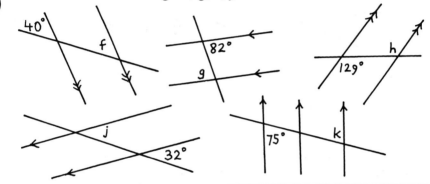

c Find the size of each angle l, m, n, p, q, r, s, t, u, v

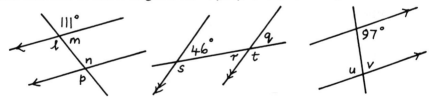

d Find the size of each angle a, b, c, d, e, f, g, h, j, k

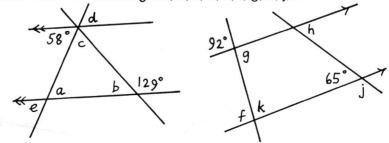

A ANGLES (6) - 'ANGLE CHASING'

SEVEN RULES TO REMEMBER (see pages 60, 62 and 64)

1) Angles in a REVOLUTION add up to 360°
2) Angles in a QUADRILATERAL add up to 360°
3) Angles on a STRAIGHT LINE add up to 180°
4) Angles in a TRIANGLE add up to 180°
5) VERTICALLY OPPOSITE angles are equal
6) CORRESPONDING angles are equal
7) ALTERNATE angles are equal

It is also useful to remember that an ISOSCELES TRIANGLE has TWO equal sides and TWO equal angles.
Note carefully which two angles are equal

B Naming an angle

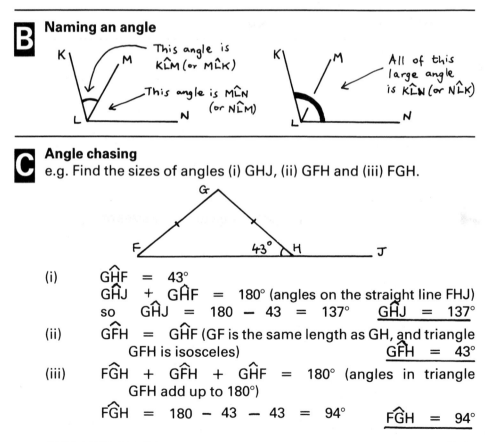

This angle is KL̂M (or ML̂K)

This angle is ML̂N (or NL̂M)

All of this large angle is KL̂N (or NL̂K)

C Angle chasing

e.g. Find the sizes of angles (i) GHJ, (ii) GFH and (iii) FGH.

(i) $\hat{GHF}$ = 43°
       $\hat{GHJ}$ + $\hat{GHF}$ = 180° (angles on the straight line FHJ)
       so $\hat{GHJ}$ = 180 − 43 = 137° $\underline{\hat{GHJ} = 137°}$

(ii) $\hat{GFH}$ = $\hat{GHF}$ (GF is the same length as GH, and triangle
       GFH is isosceles) $\underline{\hat{GFH} = 43°}$

(iii) $\hat{FGH}$ + $\hat{GFH}$ + $\hat{GHF}$ = 180° (angles in triangle
       GFH add up to 180°)
       $\hat{FGH}$ = 180 − 43 − 43 = 94° $\underline{\hat{FGH} = 94°}$

IF IN DIFFICULTY fill in **ANY** angles which you can work out. This may help you to find the one you want.

COPY THE DIAGRAMS ROUGHLY AND FILL IN ON YOUR COPY
THE ANGLE SIZES AS YOU FIND THEM

a Find the sizes of angles BDC, ABC and BCD

Write your answer   BD̂C =
AB̂C =
BĈD =

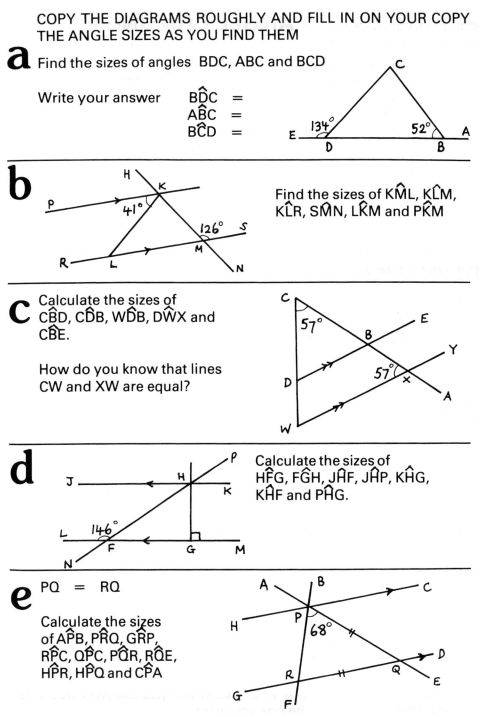

b Find the sizes of KM̂L, KL̂M,
KL̂R, SM̂N, LK̂M and PK̂M

c Calculate the sizes of
CB̂D, CD̂B, WD̂B, DŴX and
CB̂E.

How do you know that lines
CW and XW are equal?

d Calculate the sizes of
HF̂G, FĜH, JÂF, JĤP, KĤG,
KĤF and PĤG.

e PQ = RQ

Calculate the sizes
of AP̂B, PR̂Q, GR̂P,
RP̂C, QP̂C, PQ̂R, RQ̂E,
HP̂R, HP̂Q and CP̂A

A POLYGONS (Many-sided figures)

A POLYGON is a plane figure with 3 or more sides.
A REGULAR POLYGON is a polygon with all its sides the same length and all its angles the same size.

5 sided figure is a PENTAGON	8 sided figure is an OCTAGON
6 sided figure is a HEXAGON	9 sided figure is a NONAGON
7 sided figure is a HEPTAGON	10 sided figure is a DECAGON

B EXTERIOR ANGLES of any polygon add up to 360°

e.g.

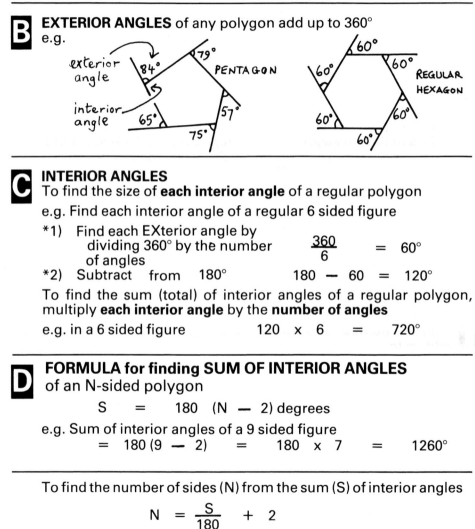

C INTERIOR ANGLES

To find the size of **each interior angle** of a regular polygon

e.g. Find each interior angle of a regular 6 sided figure

*1)   Find each EXterior angle by
      dividing 360° by the number
      of angles
      $$\frac{360}{6} = 60°$$

*2)   Subtract   from   180°   180 — 60 = 120°

To find the sum (total) of interior angles of a regular polygon, multiply **each interior angle** by the **number of angles**

e.g. in a 6 sided figure   120 x 6   =   720°

D FORMULA for finding SUM OF INTERIOR ANGLES

of an N-sided polygon

$$S = 180 \ (N - 2) \text{ degrees}$$

e.g. Sum of interior angles of a 9 sided figure
     = 180 (9 — 2)   =   180 x 7   =   1260°

To find the number of sides (N) from the sum (S) of interior angles

$$N = \frac{S}{180} + 2$$

e.g. How many sides has a polygon whose interior angles add up to 1980°?

$$N = \frac{1980}{180} + 2 = 13 \text{ sides}$$

a Find the size of each **exterior** angle of
1) a regular pentagon
2) a regular octagon
3) a regular 12 sided figure
4) a regular 20 sided figure
5) a regular nonagon
6) a regular decagon
7) a regular 36 sided figure
8) a regular (square) quadrilateral
9) a regular 16 sided figure
10) a regular (equilateral) triangle

---

b Find the size of each **interior** angle of
1) a regular octagon
2) a regular 15 sided figure
3) a regular hexagon
4) a regular quadrilateral
5) a regular 30 sided figure
6) a regular 12 sided figure
7) a regular pentagon
8) a regular 24 sided figure
9) a regular decagon
10) a regular nonagon

---

c Find the **sum** of the interior angles of
1) a decagon
2) a heptagon
3) a 20 sided figure
4) a triangle
5) pentagon
6) a 14 sided figure
7) a 22 sided figure
8) a quadrilateral
9) an 11 sided figure
10) a 17 sided figure

---

d Find the number of sides of the polygon whose interior angles add up to
1) 720°
2) 2340°
3) 1080°
4) 1800°
5) 1260°

---

e
1) The sum of the interior angles of a polygon is 2520°. How many sides has the polygon?
2) Four of the interior angles of a pentagon have sizes 96°, 104°, 117° and 150°. Find the size of the other interior angle
3) Each exterior angle of a certain regular polygon is 24°. How many sides has the polygon?
4) Each interior angle of a certain regular polygon is 160°. How many sides has the polygon?
5) Four of the interior angles of a hexagon are 105°, 109°, 134° and 138°. The other two angles are equal. What size is each of the missing angles?

SOME EXTRA QUESTIONS

1) Write in 24 hour clock notation (a) 8.50 p.m. (b) 12.18 a.m. (c) 1.47 p.m.

2) Calculate the sizes of angles v and w (not drawn to scale)

3) Find the union of each of these pairs of sets
   (a) $\{\frac{1}{2}, \frac{1}{4}, \frac{1}{3}, \frac{1}{5}, \frac{1}{6}\}$, $\{\frac{1}{6}, \frac{1}{3}, \frac{1}{2}, \frac{2}{3}, \frac{5}{6}\}$
   (b) $\{O, \mathbf{O}, \ominus, \bullet\}$, $\{\mathbf{O}, \oplus, \ominus\}$

4) (a) $307_9 + 58_9 + 461_9$ (b) $2163_8 - 707_8$

5) A train travelled from Stoke-on-Trent to London, a distance of 150 miles, at an average speed of 72 miles/hour. How long, in hours and minutes, did its journey take?

6) Find the size of (a) each exterior (b) each interior, angle of a regular 18 sided figure

7) Find the average of 16, 23, 18, 20, 15, 17, 22 and 21

8) Copy the questions and complete them with the correct answers
   $D \cap C$ = ... $n(C)$ = ...
   $D \cup C$ = ... $(D \cup C)'$ = ...
   C' = ...

9) Write as a number of minutes (i) $\frac{11}{15}$ hour, (ii) $7\frac{1}{2}$ hours (iii) $\frac{5}{12}$ hour

10) Calculate the sizes of angles a,b,c,d and e (not drawn to scale)

11) (a) Add 1 hour 55 min, 2 hours 23 min, 2 hours 48 min
    (b) Multiply 5 hours 27 minutes by 4

12) (i) Find the next eight consecutive numbers above 21 in base 3
    (ii) Find the next three consecutive numbers below 101 in base 5

13) Draw a Venn diagram to show $\mathcal{E}$ = $\{a, b, c, d, e, f, g\}$
    W = $\{b, c, d\}$, Z = $\{c, d, e, f\}$

14) Make a rough larger copy of each of these angles and write what kind each angle is (e.g. acute angle)

15) (a) $11101_2 \times 101_2$ (b) $1101101_2 - 10110_2$

16) Express as a fraction of an hour in its lowest terms
    (i) 21 minutes   (ii) 6 minutes   (iii) 56 minutes

17) Find (a) the H.C.F. and (b) the L.C.M. of 198 and 108. Draw a Venn diagram to show the prime factors

18) A length of motorway began to be built in November 1984 and was finished 2 years 5 months later. In which month of which year was it finished?

19) Write   (a) 1222_3 in denary   (b) 327_{10} in base 6

20) Calculate the speed (S) from each distance (D) and time (T)
   (i) D = 750 miles, T = 12 hours
   (ii) D = 23.4 metres, T = 1.8 seconds

21) Calculate the sizes of $L\hat{K}N$, $M\hat{L}N$ and $J\hat{K}N$ (not drawn to scale)

22) Write in short, using the correct sign instead of each group of underlined words
   (a) moth is a member of the set of insects
   (b) G is a subset of M
   (c) A = an empty set, so the number of members of A = 0

23) (i) Express 15 metres/second in km/hour
   (ii) Express 810 km/hour in metres/second

24) A bus set off at 1445 and travelled for 3 hours 38 minutes. At what time did it complete its journey?

25) (a) $431_5 \times 42_5$ (b) $223_4 + 303_4 + 321_4$

26) For each of these groups of sets, draw the best possible Venn diagram and write each number in its correct region
   (i) A = {32, 22, 16, 11, 8},   B = {2.8, 4, 5.6, 8, 11}
   (ii) $\mathcal{E}$ = {1,2,3,4,5,6,7,8,9},   G = {3,6,9},   H = {1,2,4,8}

27) (a) Subtract 5 years 9 months from 10 years 7 months
   (b) Divide 14 years 8 months by 4

28) Find the average of $\frac{3}{4}$, $\frac{5}{8}$, $\frac{7}{24}$ and $\frac{2}{3}$

29) By converting TO DENARY first, express 263_7 as a number in base 3

30) What is the sum of the interior angles of
   (i) a 12 sided figure?   (ii) a 19 sided figure?

31) A car travelled for 3 hours 40 minutes at an average speed of 42 miles/hour. How far did it travel?

32) Draw a copy of this Venn diagram. Write the correct number of members in each region

34 words (set $\mathcal{E}$), 17 words beginning with S (set S), 20 French words (set F), 11 French words beginning with S (set S ∩ F)

33) (a) Add in binary 11010_2, 101110_2, and 1101_2
   (b) Divide 111001_2 by 11_2

34) Write in a.m. or p.m. notation (a) 0245, (b) 2121, (c) 1207

35) Calculate the sizes of angles G and H (not drawn to scale)

36) Write down the first sixteen numbers in base 4, starting with 1

37) For each of these pairs of sets, draw a Venn diagram showing the subset inside the larger set
   (a)   {P, Q, R, S, T, V}, {P,R,V}
   (b)   {27, 30}, {26, 27, 28, 29, 30, 31, 32}

38) Express as hours and fractions of an hour
   (i)   2 hours 27 minutes   (ii)   8 hours 36 minutes

39) (a) $345_6 \times 43_6$ (b) $1425_7 \div 6$

40) Find the angle between the hands of a clock at
   (a)   4 o'clock   (b)   7.30   (c)   2.10

41) Make a larger copy of this Venn diagram. Write the correct NUMBER of members in each region.
   $\mathcal{E}$ = {animals},   L = {large animals},   B = {brown animals}, F = {furry animals}
   70 animals altogether; 11 large brown furry animals; 8 large furry animals which are not brown; 15 brown furry animals which are not large; 40 furry animals altogether; 7 large animals which are not brown and not furry; 35 large animals altogether; 10 animals which are not large, not brown and not furry

42) Express 61_{10} in   (a) binary   (b) octal

43) The average mass of six boys was 42kg. The masses of five of the boys were 53kg, 46kg, 44kg, 37kg and 34kg. What was the mass of the other boy?

44)

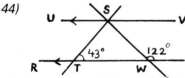

Calculate the sizes of $S\hat{W}T$, $V\hat{S}W$, $R\hat{T}S$, $U\hat{S}T$ and $T\hat{S}W$ (not drawn to scale)

45) David ran 1500 metres in exactly 6 minutes. Calculate his speed in metres/second.

46) Make a list of all the subsets of {j, k, l, m}

47) Convert   (a) 922_{10} to base 9   (b) 465_7 to denary

48) Four of the angles in a heptagon are 93°, 105°, 144° and 159°. The other three angles are equal. What size is each of the other angles?

49) If J = {2, 5, 8, 11, 14},   K = {2, 3, 5, 7, 11, 13}, find (i) J ∩ K,   (ii) J ∪ K,   (iii) n(K)

50) An aeroplane took off from Dallas at 2235 and flew 632 miles to Denver to an average speed of 237 miles/hour. At what time did it arrive in Denver?